ATOMIC ABSORPTION SPECTROMETRY IN GEOLOGY

SERIES

Methods in Geochemistry and Geophysics

1. A. S. RITCHIE
CHROMATOGRAPHY IN GEOLOGY

2. R. BOWEN
PALEOTEMPERATURE ANALYSIS

3. D. S. PARASNIS
MINING GEOPHYSICS

4. I. ADLER
X-RAY EMISSION SPECTROGRAPHY IN GEOLOGY

5. THE LORD ENERGLYN AND L. BREALEY
ANALYTICAL GEOCHEMISTRY

6. A. J. EASTON
CHEMICAL ANALYSIS OF SILICATE ROCKS

8. A. VOLBORTH
ELEMENTAL ANALYSIS IN GEOCHEMISTRY
A. MAJOR ELEMENTS

9. P. K. BHATTACHARYA AND H. P. PATRA
DIRECT CURRENT GEOELECTRIC SOUNDING

10. J. A. S. ADAMS AND P. GASPARINI
GAMMA-RAY SPECTROMETRY OF ROCKS

11. W. ERNST
GEOCHEMICAL FACIES ANALYSIS

Methods in Geochemistry and Geophysics

7

ATOMIC ABSORPTION SPECTROMETRY IN GEOLOGY

BY

ERNEST E. ANGINO

Chairman, Department of Geology; Professor of Geology and Civil Engineering The University of Kansas, Lawrence, Kansas, U.S.A.

AND

GALE K. BILLINGS

Head, Department of Geosciences; Professor of Geochemistry, New Mexico Institute of Mining and Technology, Socorro, New Mexico, U.S.A.

SECOND REVISED EDITION 1972

ELSEVIER PUBLISHING COMPANY

AMSTERDAM/LONDON/NEW YORK

1972

ELSEVIER PUBLISHING COMPANY
335 JAN VAN GALENSTRAAT, P.O. BOX 211, AMSTERDAM

AMERICAN ELSEVIER PUBLISHING COMPANY, INC.
52 VANDERBILT AVENUE, NEW YORK, N.Y. 10017

FIRST EDITION 1967
SECOND REVISED EDITION 1972

LIBRARY OF CONGRESS CATALOG CARD NUMBER 67-25748

ISBN 0 444 41012 0 (SECOND REVISED EDITION)

WITH 14 ILLUSTRATIONS AND 38 TABLES

PRINTED IN THE NETHERLANDS

Preface to the Second Edition

Both the first and second editions of this book are not solely the result of the author's endeavors. We have profited greatly by the generosity and experience of other scientists in the field of atomic absorption. For their support and encouragement we would like to thank the scientists of both the Perkin-Elmer Corporation and the Jarrell-Ash Company, Division of Fisher Industries. For many valuable discussions concerning applications, we owe a debt of gratitude to Dr. Paul C. Ragland, University of North Carolina; Dr. R.C. Harriss, Florida State University; Mr. Walter Slavin, Perkin-Elmer Corporation; Mr. J.C. Nicola, Atlantic-Richfield Corporation; and Mr. O.K. Galle, State Geological Survey of Kansas. We wish to thank here all those organizations which so kindly allowed us to use copyrighted material when it was needed.

The work of the senior author has been encouraged both in the preparation of the first edition and now the second edition of this book by the Director of the State Geological Survey of Kansas and the Chairman of the Dept. of Civil Engineering of The University of Kansas. Without this support this revised volume would not have been completed. The junior author's experience has been supported by, and is therefore a result of, Rice University, Sinclair Oil and Gas Company, The University of Calgary, The National Research Council of Canada, Louisiana State University, and New Mexico Institute of Mining and Technology. Mrs. Diana Coleman typed the many drafts of both the original and revised manuscripts and for her patience special thanks are due. It is our pleasure to acknowledge this support.

Much has been accomplished since the first edition in applying atomic absorption techniques to the solution of problems in geology and geochemistry. To attempt a discussion of the literally hundreds of papers published on the subject since 1966 would be impossible. Many of these papers describe routine applications and need not be mentioned further. What we have endeavored to accomplish is a review of those papers which we felt were especially pertinent and made a significant contribution toward advancing the field. In this only time can be the judge of how well we succeeded. If we have omitted something of value, it was not intentional and we beg both the reader's and the original author's indulgence.

The critical review of the original manuscript by Dr. Paul C. Ragland and of portions of revised version by Mr. O. Karmie Galle was most beneficial. It would be nice to know that all errors have been eliminated, however, try as we did, we know from experience some errors will remain. For these we take all blame.

For their support, encouragement, and most definitely patience, we owe much to our wives and families. The preparation of both the first and second editions of this book has been both enjoyable and scientifically rewarding. It is our sincere hope that the reader will accrue both of these benefits.

ERNEST E. ANGINO
GALE K. BILLINGS

October, 1971

Contents

PART I

Theory and Instrumentation

CHAPTER I

Introduction

The trend in geology is toward quantification in the investigation of geologic principles and concepts. Concomitant with this trend has been the increased use of chemical analytical techniques in the study of chemical petrology, chemical weathering, ore solutions, and related subjects. Of special interest in such studies is knowledge of the major and trace element content and distribution within rocks, minerals, and other natural materials.

The increase in the use of atomic absorption for the determination of major and trace elements in rocks, minerals, ores, and waters has been spectacular. During the last five years, atomic absorption spectrometry has proven to be a very useful tool for the quantitative determination of more than 45 metallic and semi-metallic elements (Fig.1). In many ways, atomic absorption might well be considered

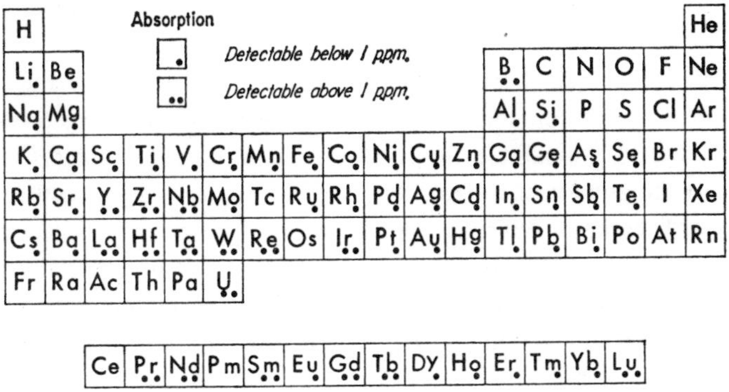

Absorption
(•) *Detectable below 1 ppm.*
(••) *Detectable above 1 ppm.*

H He
Li Be B C N O F Ne
Na Mg Al Si P S Cl Ar
K Ca Sc Ti V Cr Mn Fe Co Ni Cu Zn Ga Ge As Se Br Kr
Rb Sr Y Zr Nb Mo Tc Ru Rh Pd Ag Cd In Sn Sb Te I Xe
Cs Ba La Hf Ta W Re Os Ir Pt Au Hg Tl Pb Bi Po At Rn
Fr Ra Ac Th Pa U

Ce Pr Nd Pm Sm Eu Gd Tb Dy Ho Er Tm Yb Lu

Fig.1. Elements detectable by atomic absorption spectrometry. Modified from *Beckman Instruments Bull.* 7071. (Published by courtesy of Beckman Instrument Inc.)

one of the better methods now available for analysis of metals; considering the number of elements covered, the simplicity of operation, sensitivity, reliability, and initial monetary investment.

It may be somewhat premature to write a book on atomic absorption spectrometry in geology, inasmuch as the field is still young and progressing rapidly. However, in comparison with other analytical techniques, there exists a relative shortage of papers on the application of the technique to geology. In many instances this is due to the relative simplicity of the method, which discourages formal publication.

This book has been written for several reasons: (*1*) partly to fill the publication gap noted previously; (*2*) to introduce geologists to the basic simplicity and applicability of atomic absorption spectrometry as it relates to geologic problems; (*3*) to provide a summary of applications of atomic absorption to geology that are at present scattered throughout the literature; and (*4*) to encourage the accelerated application of atomic absorption spectrometry to geological problems.

Atomic absorption is the absorption of radiant energy by ground state atoms. Substances when dispersed as an atomic vapor possess the property of absorbing characteristic radiations identical to that which the same substance can emit. It is this property that forms the basis of what has been termed "atomic absorption spectroscopy".

The general lack of spectral or chemical interferences is a primary advantage of atomic absorption spectrometry. Most of the problems exist in the sample preparation and although problems do exist in the analytical system, they are more amenable to solution than with flame or emission spectrography. The excellent spectral resolution of the instrumentation results in a high degree of element specificity. The sensitivity rivals that of most other methods and trace element analysis at sub-p.p.m. levels in solutions is common for many elements.

Operation of atomic absorption instrumentation is quite simple. However, development of new applications and maximum yield from known applications requires knowledge of atomic absorption theory and instrumentation. For this reason, we have included chapters on these subjects. Discussion of the theory has been simplified from that normally found in spectroscopic publications. We have, however, endeavored to present enough theory to provide the geologist with a basic understanding of the physical principles pertinent to atomic absorption spectrometry.

We have included here only those applications which have been or would be carried out by geologists and geochemists. For example, we have excluded those techniques (which are numerous) pertaining to soil and biochemical analysis.

We have presented a rather detailed chapter on interferences and interference tests. Although interferences are minimal, the results of tests are not always negative; consequently, we thought that this chapter would allow any analyst to compare his sample with the tests presented and thus be able to predict potential interferences.

The book is divided into two parts, one on "Theory and instrumentation" and one on "Methods and applications". By no means can the material presented herein be considered final. We should again stress that in a field as vigorous as atomic absorption analysis, changes and improvements are certain to come rapidly.

CHAPTER 2

Theory

The theory of atomic absorption spectrophotometry has been lucidly presented by WALSH (1961) and by ELWELL and GIDLEY (1962).

RELATIONSHIP OF ATOMIC ABSORPTION TO ATOMIC CONCENTRATION

The following presentation is restricted to the more fundamental physical relationships and to atomic absorption lines possessing no hyperfine structure. The physics of the relationships between atomic concentration and atomic absorption are more fully discussed by MITCHELL and ZEMANSKY (1934) and ROSSELAND (1936).

Assume a parallel radiant beam of intensity $I_{o\nu}$ at frequency ν passing through an atomic vapor l cm thick. If I_ν is the intensity of the transmitted beam, the absorption coefficient, K, at frequency ν is defined by

$$I_\nu = I_{o\nu} \exp(-K_\nu l) \qquad (1)$$

The dependence of K_ν on ν is determined by the electron shell transition during absorption and on such conditions as the temperature, pressure, and electrical fields affecting the atoms. These effects are discussed in subsequent sections.

The relationship between concentration and the integrated absorption coefficient is given by:

$$\int K_\nu \mathrm{d}\nu = \frac{\pi e^2}{mc} N_\nu f \qquad (2)$$

where f is the oscillator strength (average number of electrons per atom that can be excited by the incident radiation), N_v the number of atoms per cm^3 which are capable of absorbing in the frequency range ν to $d\nu$, c the velocity of light, m the electronic mass, and e the electronic charge.

Considering a transition from a state i of excitation energy E_i, the number of atoms per cm^3 capable of absorbing (N_v) is related to the total number of atoms per cm^3 (N) by:

$$N_v = N \frac{P_i \exp(-E_i/kT)}{\sum P_j \exp(-E_j/kT)} \qquad (3)$$

where P_i and P_j are the statistical weights of the initial and other energy states; (i.e., the degree of degeneracy of the energy states) respectively, k = Boltzmann's constant, T = absolute temperature in °K, and the summation is over all possible energy states.

WALSH (1955) has shown that the fraction of the total available atoms which exist in the excited state becomes appreciable only for atoms with low ionization potentials and at high temperatures. Most elements have their strongest resonance lines at wave lengths below 6,000 Å (see Table II), and since atomic absorption measurements are usually made at flame temperatures below 3,000°C, the number of atoms in the ground state generally can be assumed to equal the number of atoms, i.e., $N_v = N$. The resonance lines are those spectral lines absorbed by atoms in the ground state. Since the vast majority of atoms are in the ground state, an inherent increase in sensitivity is accrued if absorption of the resonance line is measured. Under these conditions, N_v in eq.2 can be replaced by N. This leads to a simple linear relationship between concentration and the integrated absorption coefficient. However, measurement of the integrated absorption coefficient cannot be accomplished satisfactorily because of experimental difficulties associated with measurement of the variations in atomic spectral characteristics. Therefore, the usual procedure is to measure peak absorption rather than the integrated absorption.

VARIATIONS IN SHAPES AND WIDTHS OF ATOMIC SPECTRAL LINES

Natural width

For resonance lines, the natural width is of the order of 10^{-4}Å. For the experimental conditions of standard atomic absorption analysis, this width is negligible when compared to variations resulting from other causes, and need not be considered further.

Doppler width

Considering a line of wave length λ, the Doppler width, D_λ, or the line broadening resulting from atoms having different component velocities along the line of observation is given by:

$$D_\lambda = 1.67 \frac{\lambda}{C} \left(\frac{2RT}{M}\right)^{\frac{1}{2}} \tag{4}$$

where M is the atomic weight, T the absolute temperature in °K, R the universal gas constant, and C the velocity of light. Since D_λ is a function of $T^{\frac{1}{2}}$, minor fluctuations in flame temperature are not a problem in atomic absorption spectrophotometry.

TABLE I

VALUES OF D_λ AT VARIOUS TEMPERATURES[1]

Element	λ (Å)	*M*	D_λ 1,000°K (Å)	D_λ 2,000°K (Å)	D_λ 3,000°K (Å)
Na	5,890	22.3	0.028	0.039	0.048
Cu	3,247	63.6	0.0092	0.0113	0.016
Zn	2,139	65.4	0.0060	0.0085	0.010

[1] Data from WALSH (1961); reproduced by permission of Interscience Publishers Inc.

The data of Table I illustrate that in the temperature range of interest (1,500–3,000°K) the Doppler width is of the order of 0.01–0.05 Å.

Pressure broadening due to foreign gases

Perturbation of the absorbing or emitting atoms by flame gas atoms causes broadening of atomic spectral lines. With an increase in the content of flame gas, the peak of the line shifts to longer wave lengths. As a first approximation, the magnitude of each of these effects is linearly proportional to gas pressure, and varies for different elements, different gases, and different atomic lines. It has so far proved impossible to calculate accurately the magnitude of the effect in any specific case (WALSH, 1961). A working rule is that for the strongest resonance lines the broadening caused by one atmosphere of a particular gas is in the range 0.01–0.1 Å. At temperatures of 1,500–3,000°K, pressure broadening is the same order of magnitude as Doppler broadening. During standard analysis, the pressure broadening will be a constant factor causing a constant proportional lowering of absorption. That is, the linear relationship between absorption and concentration will be maintained but the analytical sensitivity will be reduced.

Resonance broadening

Resonance broadening is a special type of pressure broadening resulting from perturbation of the emitting or absorbing atom by an atom of the same type. Resonance broadening is more of a problem in atomic absorption analysis than is normal pressure broadening. With an increase in the concentration of the sample vapor, there is a corresponding reduction in proportional absorption. The reduction is not a linear function of concentration and therefore will destroy the linear relation between concentration and absorption. The result will be a curvature of the calibration graph towards the concentration axis (Fig.2).

Self-absorption broadening

An important cause of line broadening is self-absorption of the emitted resonance lines in the hollow cathode tubes (tubes are described in a subsequent section). Self-absorption broadening can

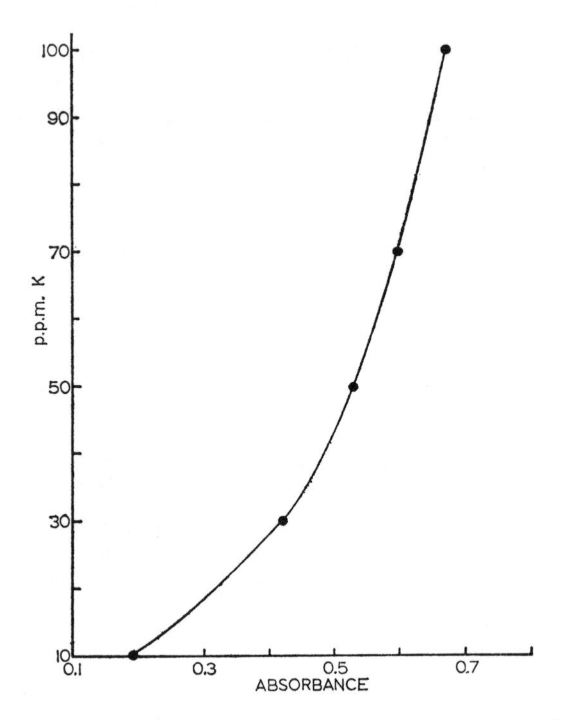

Fig.2. Curvature of calibration graph at high concentrations (G. K. Billings, unpublished data).

be minimized by using combinations of source length and vapor concentrations which reduce the absorption along the length of the source. Self-reversal is a special type of broadening that occurs when the source is surrounded by a cooler sheath of vapor, and results in selective absorption of the center of the line.

Stark broadening

The splitting of a single spectrum line into multiple lines, which occurs when the emitting material is placed in a strong electrical field, is termed the Stark effect. The separation increases with the field strength. A non-uniform field will produce a series of Stark components and result in broadening of the line. Since the electric field is small in standard atomic absorption procedures, it is not generally a serious cause of line broadening.

Zeeman broadening

The splitting of a spectrum line into several symmetrically disposed components, which occurs when the source of light is placed in a strong magnetic field, is termed the Zeeman effect. Its effects are only appreciable under strong externally applied fields and are negligible under standard atomic absorption analytical conditions.

CURVATURE OF THE CALIBRATION GRAPH

One of the major causes of curvature of the calibration graph is resonance broadening, as previously noted. Other causes exist and are discussed here (MENZIES, 1960; RUBESKA and SVOBODA, 1964).

Curvature may arise through some of the incident light falling outside the region of strong absorption. This may be caused by the emission line of the source being too broad or because the regions of flame accepted by the monochromator are all equally absorptive. In both of these cases, the absorption is relatively "diluted" by some light which escapes absorption. If i_o is the intensity of unabsorbed light then the measured absorbance will be:

$$\log \frac{I_o + i_o}{I + i_o} \tag{5}$$

instead of:

$$\log \frac{I_o}{I} \tag{5a}$$

where I_o is the intensity of the incident beam and I is the intensity of the transmitted beam, and the calibration curve will be asymptotic to the value

$$\log \frac{I_o + i_o}{I + i_o} \tag{6}$$

TABLE II

RELATIVE DETECTION LIMITS AND ANALYTICAL SENSITIVITIES[1]

Metal	*Relative detection limit (mg/l)*	*Analytical sensitivity (mg/l for 1% absorption)*	*(Å)*	*Reference*[2]
Ag	0.02	0.1	3,281	1,13
Al*	0.1	6.0	3,092	1,13
Ar	–	–	8,115	9
As	0.5	5.0	1,937	1,13
Au	0.1	0.3	2,428	1,13
B*	5.0	250	2,497	1,13
B^{11}	–	–	2,496	10
B^{10}	–	–	2,497	10
Ba	0.1	5.0	5,536	1,13
Be*	0.003	0.2	2,349	1,13
Bi	0.02	1.0	2,231	1,13
Ca	0.005	0.1	4,227	1,13
Ca	–	0.02	–	8
Cd	0.01	0.04	2,288	1
Co	0.05	0.45	2,407	1,13
Co	–	0.08	–	8
Cr	0.01	0.15	3,579	1
Cr	–	0.02	–	8
Cs**	0.05	0.5	8,521	1,13
Cu	0.005	0.2	3,247	1
Cu	–	0.02	–	8
Dy	0.2	–	4,046	12,13
Er	0.2	–	3,863	12,13
Eu	0.2	–	4,594	12,13
Fe	0.02	0.3	2,483	1,13
Fe	–	0.04	–	8
Ga	0.07	3.0	2,874	1,13
Ga	0.07	2.3	2,874	5
Gd	4.0	–	3,684	12,13
Ge	2.0	–	2,651	1,13
He	–	–	3,889	9
Hf	15.0	–	–	13
Hg***	0.5	10	2,537	1
Ho	0.3	–	4,054	12,13

TABLE II *(continued)*

Metal	*Relative detection limit (mg/l)*	*Analytical sensitivity (mg/l for 1% absorption)*	*(Å)*	*Reference*[2]
In	0.05	0.2	3,040	3,13
In	0.5	1.0	3,040	1
In	0.05	0.9	3,039	5
Ir	4.0	–	–	13
K**	0.002	0.1	7,665	1,13
K**	–	0.03	–	8
Kr	–	–	8,060	9
La	80.0	–	3,574	12, 13
Li	0.005	0.07	6,708	1, 13
Lu	–	–	2,989	12
Mg	0.003	0.015	2,852	1
Mg	–	0.001		8
Mn	0.01	0.15	2,795	1
Mn	–	0.005	–	8
Mo	0.05	1.5	3,133	1, 13
Na**	0.005	0.05	5,890	1
Nb*	2.0	250	4,059	2, 13
Nd	2.0	–	–	13
Ne	–	–	6,402	9
Ne	–	–	4,634	12
Ni	0.02	0.2	2,320	1, 13
Ni	0.01	0.09	2,320	4
Pb	0.05	0.7	2,170	1, 13
Pb	–	0.13	–	8
Pd	0.5	1.0	2,476	1, 13
Pd	–	0.3	2,448	3
Pr	10.0	–	5,133	12, 13
Pt	0.5	2.0	2,659	1
Rb**	0.02	0.2	7,800	1
Rb**	0.003	0.12	7,800	6, 13
Re*	1.5	25	3,460	3, 13
Rh	0.03	0.3	3,435	1, 13
Ru	0.3	0.25	3,499	3, 13

TABLE II *(continued)*

Metal	*Relative detection Limit (mg/l)*	*Analytical sensitivity (mg/l for 1% absorption)*	*(Å)*	*Reference*[2]
Sb	0.2	1.0	3,175	1
Sc*	0.2	5.0	3,907	2, 13
Se	1.0	3.0	1,961	1, 13
Si*	0.2	–	2,516	1
Sm	5.0	–	4,298	12, 13
Sn	0.1	1.0	2,246	7
Sr	0.02	0.2	4,607	1, 13
Ta	6.0	–	–	13
Tb	2.0	–	4,318	12, 13
Te	0.5	1.5	2,143	1
Ti*	0.2	–	3,643	1, 13
Tl**	0.2	1.0	2,768	1
Tm	0.1	–	3,718	12, 13
U	30.0	–	5,027	11, 13
V*	0.1	–	3,184	1, 13
W	3.0	–	4,008	1, 13
Xe	–	–	8,232	9
Y	0.3	–	–	13
Yb	–	–	2,465	12
Zn	0.005	0.04	2,138	1
Zn	–	0.005	–	8
Zr	5.0	–	–	13

[1] Many of the values given for certain elements will be improved by using a nitrous oxide–acetylene gas mixture.

[2] *1* = SLAVIN (1964a); *2* = FASSEL and MOSSOTTI (1963); *3* = ALLEN (1962); *4* = CARTWRIGHT et al. (1966); *5* = MULFORD (1966); *6* = SLAVIN et al. (1965); *7* = CAPACHO-DELGADO and MANNING (1965); *8* = HELL et al. (1965); *9* = GOLEB (1966a); *10* = GOLEB (1966b); *11* = GOLEB (1966c); *12* = MOSSOTTI and FASSEL (1964); *13* = SLAVIN (1966).

* An oxyacetylene flame is used.

** Osram spectral lamp.

*** G.E. OZ4 mercury lamp.

instead of infinity. This unabsorbed light (i_o) may arise in several ways: photocell dark-current; scattered light in a monochromator; and light bypassing the flame. These problems can be minimized by suitable instrumentation.

The increase in viscosity with increasing concentration can also cause curvature. This problem, which often occurs during analysis of high-salt solutions for trace constituents, can be reduced by diluting the sample, by using closely spaced standards of a viscosity comparable to the sample, or by the standard-addition method.

ANALYZABLE ELEMENTS

Research in atomic absorption spectrometry is proceeding at such a rapid pace that it is impossible to set ultimate limits of sensitivity or to eliminate any elements from consideration. Thus the information given in Table II will doubtlessly be altered in the future by improved instrumentation and techniques. Nevertheless, it is advisable to present an up-to-date summation.

CHAPTER 3

Instrumentation

INTRODUCTION

The atomic absorption spectrophotometer (Fig.3) consists basically of:

(*a*) A light source which emits the sharp-line spectrum of the element to be determined.

(*b*) A method to produce atomic vapor of the sample to be analyzed.

(*c*) A wavelength selector to isolate the resonance lines.

(*d*) A detector, amplifier, and readout system.

In further sections of this chapter, we will discuss each of the components in detail. An excellent, brief review of instrumentation has been given by KAHN (1966).

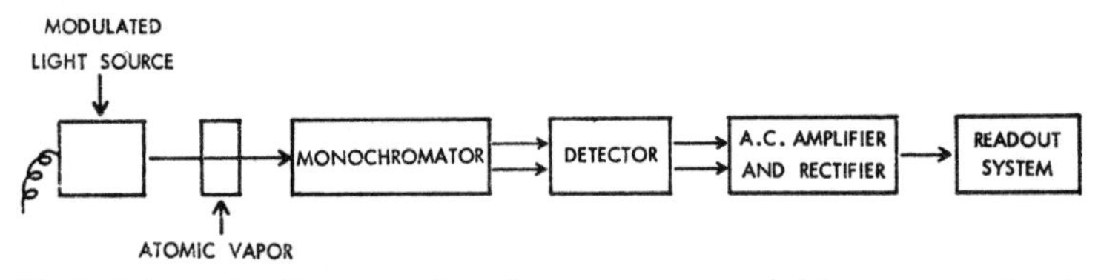

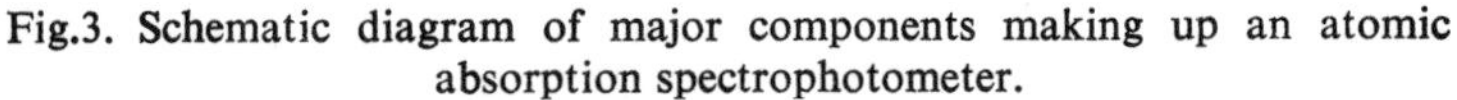

Fig.3. Schematic diagram of major components making up an atomic absorption spectrophotometer.

LIGHT SOURCES

Spectral vapor lamps

For the more volatile elements, such as thallium, mercury, and most of the alkalies, the usual light source is the spectral vapor lamp. In this lamp, an arc is struck between two electrodes in the vapor of the metal thus causing emission of the desired wavelengths. To minimize self-reversal, the lamp must normally be operated at the lowest current which gives a stable discharge.

Hollow cathode tubes

Hollow cathode tubes are at present the most satisfactory sources for the less volatile elements. A hollow cathode tube consists of an anode and a hollow cylindrical cathode containing, or lined with, the metal whose spectrum is desired. These electrodes are in a sealed tube, with a glass or quartz window, and filled with one of the inert gases at low pressure. The tube is connected to a source of electrical current. The discharge takes place within the hollow cathode, and bombardment by the inert gas atoms causes free atoms to sputter off the cathode. These atoms are excited by collision with the inert gas atoms and emit the desired sharp-line spectrum.

SULLIVAN and WALSH (1965) have described a new type of hollow cathode tube which emits resonance lines of some hundreds-fold increase in intensity without increase in line-width. The essential difference from standard hollow cathode tubes is that instead of using one electrical discharge to produce the metallic vapors and excite the atoms, the new tube uses a separate isolated current for each process. In this way, increasing the excitation of the vapor by increased current does not lead to increased vapor pressure and, therefore, to self-absorption. This type of high-intensity lamp yields a much more linear working curve in concentrated solutions of the element to be determined and yields increased sensitivity.

Multi-element tubes have recently been produced commercially. The economic advantages of multi-element hollow cathode tubes are obvious. In addition, there is an improvement in warm-up time of the tube if more than one element can be placed in one hollow cathode tube. SEBENS et al. (1964) have examined the characteristics of a Ni–Co–Fe–Cu–Cr–Mn hollow cathode tube. They report that lamp life is similar to conventional tubes and that performance is only slightly inferior. The major problem is resolution of the desired resonance lines from the complex spectra produced. MANNING et al. (1965) have described a Ca–Mg hollow cathode tube as being satisfactory with respect to sensitivity, lamp life, and emission energy.

Other light sources

GOLEB (1966a) has described a technique for producing a light source which he used to determine the atomic absorption spectra of the noble gases. A Schüler–Gollnow, water-cooled, hollow-cathode emission tube (TOLANSKY, 1947) was operated at 30 ma with a gas pressure of 2 mm Hg for the various noble gases. The emitted light was modulated and focussed on the hole of a copper insert that was the cathode electrode of the absorption tube. The absorption tube employed various gas pressures of the noble gases and absorption of the incident light was thus obtained. The amount of transmitted light coming from the absorption tube was then measured with a spectrophotometer. GOLEB (1963, 1966c, d), GOLEB and BRODY (1963), and GOLEB and YOKOYAMA (1964) have also used this technique in studies of Li, U, and B isotopes by atomic absorption (see Chapter 9).

The Schüler-Gollnow hollow cathode source has also been used to examine the spectra of F, S, C1, and O (MCNALLY et al., 1947). Sensitivities were in the p.p.m. range. The spectral lines used were within the range normally covered by atomic absorption monochromators although the principal resonance lines of these elements are in the visible-ultraviolet. The application of the atomic absorption technique to analysis for these elements should be reinvestigated, as their geochemistry is poorly understood and their determination by present means is time-consuming and rather difficult.

FASSEL et al. (1966) have investigated the use of a spectral continuum as a light source for numerous elements. The method makes use of a three-burner, multi-pass optical system. The light sources used were a Xenon arc and a Tungsten filament lamp. The data of Table III compare the detection limits of hollow cathode

TABLE III

COMPARISON OF DETECTION LIMITS[1]

Element	*Continuum*	*Hollow cathode*
Ag	0.2	0.02
Bi	4	0.2
Co	3	0.15
Cr	0.2	0.01
Cs	0.2	0.05
Cu	0.05	0.005
Fe	1	0.02
K	0.03	0.002
Na	0.03	0.005
Ni	0.7	0.02
Pb	2	0.15
Al	2	0.5
Ba	0.9	0.1
Ca	0.03	0.005
Ga	2	0.07
Ho	2	0.35
In	0.2	0.05
Li	0.004	0.005
Mg	0.01	0.003
Mn	0.07	0.01
Mo	0.8	0.05
Rb	0.04	0.003
Sn	6	2
Sr	0.06	0.02
Ti	5	2
Tl	0.6	0.2
V	0.6	1
Dy	0.5	5.3
Er	1	0.2
Eu	0.4	0.2
Gd	60	4
Lu	50	5.0
Nb	30	20
Nd	40	2
Pr	60	0.5
Re	5	1.5
Sc	1	0.2
Sm	10	5
Tb	30	2
Tm	0.1	0.1
Y	10	0.3
Yb	0.2	0.04

[1] Limits in mg/l (the reader should consult FASSEL et al., 1966, for details of this table). Modified by addition of data from SLAVIN (1966).

methods (SLAVIN, 1964a) to those of a continuum source (FASSEL et al., 1966). The continuum source generally compares favorably with the hollow cathode and in some cases is more sensitive. As a result of the cost of maintaining a supply of all available hollow cathode tubes as well as loss of warm-up time for the tubes, the use of a continuum as a light source holds great promise.

BUTLER and STRASHEIM (1965) have described a personally-built apparatus for simultaneous multiple-element analysis. The instrument makes use of movable detectors, a quartz spectrograph, and multiple-element hollow cathode tubes. Best results were obtained using internal standards or a non-resonance line as a monitor. The method was used for the determination of Cu and Ag in Au, and for the determination of Pb, Ni, Fe, and Zn in copper-base alloys.

BRECH (1965) has described a multi-channel atomic absorption spectrometer developed by the Jarrell–Ash Company. The instrument is designed to simultaneously provide data for ten elements. Up to four hollow-cathode tubes can be used and these may be multi-element tubes. Each analytical spectral line is isolated by an exit slit mounted to a movable bracket. A photomultiplier is located behind each exit slit and each is mounted on a focal curve of matching radius. The readout can be a single meter that is manually connected to each channel in turn, or a more complex multiple-readout can be used.

SAMPLE VAPORIZATION

Although there are several methods of vaporizing materials directly from the solid state, most investigators vaporize the sample by spraying a solution of the material into a flame. For this reason, flames and burners will be discussed first.

Flame position

RANN and HAMBLY (1965) have examined the distribution of atoms in a characteristic (10 cm) atomic absorption flame. They investigated the distribution of Cu, Mo, Mg, Cr, Ca, Ag, Sr, Ba,

Na, and Se and clearly demonstrated that maximum absorption is a function of light beam position in the flame coupled with the fuel/air ratio of the flame. Their results are tabulated in Table IV.

TABLE IV

DISTRIBUTION OF ATOMS IN 10-CM AIR-ACETYLENE FLAME[1]

	Height[2] *(cm)*	
Element	*Fuel-rich*	*Air-rich*
Cu	1.4	0.5
Mo	1.1	0.35
Mg	2.0	1.0
Cr	1.0	0.35
Ca	2.4	0.7
Ag	1.5	1.1
Sr	1.6	0.65
Ba	1.2	0.6
Na	0.65	0.5
Se	1.6	0.6
OH		0.3

[1] Heights are visually approximated by the present authors (see RANN and HAMBLY, 1965). Reproduced by permission of *Anal. Chem.*
[2] Height given is that for the maximum number of absorbing atoms in the flame.

The effect of flame height on sensitivity of Mg has also been demonstrated by ANDREW and NICHOLLS (1962). In an effort to increase sensitivity, methods have been devised to pass the light beam through the flame several times by using mirrors. If the beam is not passed through the zone of maximum absorption, increased optical noise may result rather than increased signal. Since absorption is not uniform throughout the flame, the analyst must position the flame properly for each element.

Burners and flames

The function of the burner is to present an atomized sample to the light beam. The atoms must be in the ground state, i.e., non-ionized. The desired temperature, therefore, is one at which dissociation of all molecules in the sample which contain the element being determined occurs, but at which a minimum of ionization occurs. The range of temperatures which are available with present commercial burners is given in Table V.

TABLE V

FLAME TEMPERATURES[1]

Flame	*Temperature (°K)*
Air–coal gas	1,800
Air–H_2	2,050
O_2–H_2	2,500
N_2O–H_2	2,600
Air–C_2H_2	2,350
O_2–C_2H_2	3,100
N_2O–C_2H_2	2,955
Air–propane	1,925

[1] Data reproduced by courtesy from Jarrell-Ash Report JO:RFJ, 1-66.

The Beckman type, total-consumption burners have often been used in atomic absorption. However, they are troubled in fuel-rich flames by high-background noise and in concentrated solutions by deposition on the orifice. The Jarrell–Ash Hetco burner also has a high level of background noise, but can be used with several types of fuel; e.g., air–H_2, O_2–H_2, N_2O–H_2, O_2–C_2H_2, and N_2O–C_2H_2. Knisely et al. (1963) have described a modified Beckman burner that decreases these problems. The burner is extended vertically by means of a graphite cylinder, which allows the gases to be premixed before leaving the orifice of the graphite cylinder.

A premix burner is produced by several manufacturers. It features a burner chamber in which sample, fuel, and oxidant are mixed before entering the flame. Such a burner usually leads to less turbulence and fewer clogging problems with solutions of high salt content. There is also less dependence on sample flow rate compared to the total consumption burner.

Butler (1962) has developed a plastic burner for use with highly corrosive solutions. The body of the burner is made of perspex. The top plate of the burner is metal and is exchangeable with other types of material so that the burner can be used for both propane and acetylene flames.

The fuels most generally used in atomic absorption are acetylene and propane. It is seldom necessary, for most elements, to use a high-temperature flame and, in the case of the alkalies, a low-temperature flame reduces ionization. However, other fuels such as nitrous oxide, cyanogen, and hydrogen have been used and are finding wider application. These higher temperature fuels are particularly useful in the analysis for elements which form refractory oxides, e.g., Al, Si, Ti, V, and Be. CHAKRABARTI et al. (1963) have investigated the determination of Al in oxyacetylene and oxyhydrogen flames, using an organic aerosol. The oxyacetylene flame yielded the highest sensitivity. The determination of Al, Be, V, Ti and Ba has been improved by use of a fuel-rich oxyacetylene flame (SLAVIN and MANNING, 1963). MANNING et al. (1963) and MANNING (1964) reported further studies of Al determination with oxyacetylene flames. They were able to determine Al in glass, cement and steel using a fuel-rich flame.

MANNING (1965) has discussed the development of a nitrous oxide-acetylene burner originally proposed by WILLIS (1965). The burner is used in the determination of those elements that form refractory oxides such as Al, Ti, Zr and Si; and, to a lesser extent, the alkaline earths. The use of this fuel has definitely improved sensitivities for refractory-forming elements because of the higher temperature and it can now be said that probably all of the metallic elements are determinable by atomic absorption analysis. The use of this fuel also decreases molecular absorption of the Ba spectrum by high-Ca solutions. Table VI gives recommendations of laminar flow (LF) versus high efficiency total consumption (HETCO) burners for optimum sensitivity. Recommended fuels for determining each element are also listed.

Long flame-path vaporization

FUWA et al. (1964) have used a long-tube vaporization method to increase sensitivity for the determination of Zn. The sample is

TABLE VI

COMPARISON OF OPTIMUM SENSITIVITY FOR LAMINAR FLOW AND TOTAL CONSUMPTION BURNERS AND RECOMMENDED FUELS FOR DETERMINING SPECIFIC ELEMENTS[1]

Element	*HETCO for optimum sensitivity*	*Laminar flow for optimum sensitivity*	*Both burners equally sensitive*	*Fuel*
Ag	X			H_2–air
Al		X		C_2H_2–N_2O
As	X			H_2–air
Au	X			H_2–air
B			X[2]	Hetco: H_2–air LF: C_2H_2–N_2O
Ba	X[2]			H_2–air
Be			X[2]	Hetco: H_2–N_2O LF: C_2H_2–N_2O
Bi	X			H_2–air
Ca	X			H_2–air
Ce		X		C_2H_2–N_2O
Cd	X			H_2–air
Co	X			H_2–air
Cr	X			H_2–N_2O
Cs	X			H_2–air
Cu	X			H_2–air
Dy		X		C_2H_2–N_2O
Fe	X			H_2–air
Ga	X			H_2–air
Ge		X		C_2H_2–N_2O
Gd		X		C_2H_2–N_2O
Hg	X			H_2–air
Ho		X		C_2H_2–N_2O
Hf		X		C_2H_2–N_2O
In	X			H_2–air
Ir	X			H_2–air
K	X			H_2–air
	X[2]			H_2–air
La		X		C_2H_2–N_2O
Li	X			H_2–air
	X[2]			H_2–air
Lu		X		C_2H_2–N_2O
Mg	X			H_2–air
Mn	X			H_2–air

TABLE VI *(continued)*

Element	*HETCO for optimum sensitivity*	*Laminar flow for optimum sensitivity*	*Both burners equally sensitive*	*Fuel*
Mo		X		C_2H_2–N_2O
Na	X			H_2–air
	X[2]			H_2–air
Nb		X		C_2H_2–N_2O
Ni	X			H_2–air
Nd		X		C_2H_2–N_2O
Os			X	LF: C_2H_2–air Hetco: H_2–air
P	X[2]			H_2–air
Pb	X			H_2–air
Pd	X			H_2–air
Pt	X			H_2–air
Pr		X		C_2H_2–N_2O
Rb	X			H_2–air
	X[2]			H_2–air
Ru			X	Hetco: H_2–air LF: C_2H_2–air
Rh	X			H_2–air
Re		X		C_2H_2–N_2O
Sb	X			H_2–air
Sc		X		C_2H_2–N_2O
Se	X			H_2–air
Sn		X		H_2–air
Si		X		C_2H_2–N_2O
Sr	X			H_2–air
	X[2]			H_2–air
Sm		X		C_2H_2–N_2O
Ta		X		C_2H_2–N_2O
Te	X			H_2–air
Ti		X		C_2H_2–N_2O
U		X		C_2H_2–N_2O
V		X		C_2H_2–N_2O
W		X		C_2H_2–N_2O
Y		X		C_2H_2–N_2O
Yb		X		C_2H_2–N_2O
Zn		X		H_2–air
Zr		X		C_2H_2–N_2O
Totals	33	26	4	

[1] Reprinted by courtesy of Jarrell-Ash Co.
[2] Hetco with flame emmission technique

aspirated through a modified Beckman, air-hydrogen aspirator burner. The flame is directed into 23 × 1.8 cm. Alundum tube through which the light beam is also passed. They were able to obtain a detection of 0.002 μg/ml (for 1% deflection of the meter).

KOIRTYOHANN and FELDMAN (1964) have further investigated this method and have modified it by using a quartz tube and by testing fuel-rich oxy-hydrogen and oxyacetylene flames. Table VII presents the results of their study.

TABLE VII

LONG-PATH CONCENTRATIONS FOR 1% ABSORPTION IN AQUEOUS SOLUTION[1]

Element	*μg/ml*
Bi	0.1
Cd	0.001
Cu	0.005
Hg	0.5
Mg	0.001
Mn	0.005
Ni	0.01
Pb	0.02
Sb	0.1
Sr	0.1
Te	0.02
Tl	0.05
Zn	0.0005

[1] Data from KOIRTYOHANN and FELDMAN (1964). Reprinted by permission of the Society of Applied Spectroscopy.

Other vaporization methods

L'vov (1961) investigated atomic absorption by means of vaporization in a graphite crucible. The crucible was a long tube, sealed at each end with quartz windows through which the light beam was passed. The electrode, containing an evaporated solution of the sample, was inserted into the longitudinal center of the crucible. The crucible was heated to 2,000–3,000°K as the electrode was simultaneously arced with a d.c. current.

The method removes chemical interferences because of complete vaporization. The time involved in dissolving the sample is not improved over flame vaporization techniques and the actual time per analysis is greater. Although the absolute sensitivities were quite low, the relative (or useful) sensitivities were little different from those using standard techniques and the method has not found wide acceptance. Modification of the method to use a solid sample in the electrode might result in a useful technique for the determination of the inert gases.

The vaporization of solid samples by capacitor discharge lamps has been demonstrated by NELSON and KUEBLER (1963). The apparatus consisted of a cylindrically-wound capacitor discharge lamp within which are placed strips of the sample or a grid of tungsten wire upon which the sample has been deposited. The light beam used for comparison is passed through the open coil of the capacitor discharge lamp and by the sample. The lamp is flashed and generates an increase in temperature of several thousand degrees, thus vaporizing the sample. The light absorption by the vapor is recorded photographically. No quantitative data were collected but the sensitivity was estimated to be on the order of a few p.p.m. The method may hold promise where it is advantageous to use solid samples. One possible application is in the determination of total Ar in K–Ar age-dating studies.

GATEHOUSE and WALSH (1960) initiated investigations on the use of cathodic sputtering for analysis of solid samples. The sample is placed in a gas-filled tube with silica windows at each end to allow passage of the light beam. The sample is used as the cathode. They were able to develop a linear curve for 0.005–0.05% Ag in Cu.

BOLING (1966) has developed a three-slot burner which yields increased sensitivity for Ca, Cr, and Mo, and is less critical to mechanical position in the beam. Of importance to analysts of concentrated solutions, the Boling burner is less susceptible to clogging than standard burners. The Boling burner may be slightly noisier than standard burners for some elements (G. K. Billings, unpublished data).

Beckman Instruments and the Perkin–Elmer Corporation have

described a heated pre-mix burner. The spray chamber is heated by infrared radiation so that the atomized sample is vaporized. The air stream, with the evaporated mist, then passes through a water cooled, maze-type condensor. A large portion of the solvent vapor condenses at the walls, while approximately 10–20% again becomes a mist. Hence, on a percentage basis, more solvent is condensed and removed than sample. This leads to relatively more of the sample being introduced into the flame and, consequently, an increase in sensitivity.

WAVELENGTH SELECTOR

The basic requirement for a wavelength selector is separation of the desired resonance line from the other emission lines of the source. For spectra containing little but the resonance lines, e.g., the alkali spectra, a simple filter suffices. For most ultraviolet spectral analysis, and particularly for complex spectra, the most useful selector is a monochromator which can be set to pass any wavelength between ca. 1,930 and 9,000 Å. Among the elements whose resonance lines are closely surrounded by other lines are iron, nickel, and cobalt, and these require a monochromator of about 2 Å bandpass. A larger bandpass causes the absorbance curve to flatten. A smaller bandpass causes a decrease of the signal/noise ratio.

DETECTOR

Photocells are satisfactory for simple spectra of high intensity; however, a photomultiplier is essential for accurate results in the determination of heavy metals. The two photomultipliers generally available are those of the Bi–O–Ag or the Cs–Sb type cathode. Geochemists interested in either the far ultraviolet (arsenic and selenium) or the red section of the spectrum (rubidium and cesium) will obtain more sensitivity by using the Bi–O–Ag photomultiplier.

Between 2,200 and 5,800 Å, the two types of photomultipliers give similar results.

It is possible to make atomic absorption measurements on resonance lines below 3,500 Å by using direct current and feeding the output of the detector to a galvanometer. In the ultraviolet the flame emission is usually negligible or can be compensated for. It is desirable, however, to modulate the light source, either by a "chopper," or by supplying the source with alternating current or modulated direct current. The output of the detector is then fed to an a.c. amplifier whose output is rectified and fed to a meter. By these various modulation methods, any signal resulting from emission in the flame is rejected.

READOUT SYSTEM

Galvanometer

The normal readout mechanism is a galvanometer which can, if desired, be nulled manually or electronically. The nulling mechanism can then be connected with a digital readout geared to display the percent absorption. The signal to the galvanometer can be sent to a recorder if desired.

Integrating analog computer

BOLING (1965) has described an electronic system designed to integrate the amplified signal from the photomultiplier. Integrators are used for data collection which increases the signal/noise ratio. Servo-operated voltage dividers compute the signal ratios. The Beer–Lambert absorption equation is solved by a nonlinear potentiometer and the concentration is given directly in digital form. Such an apparatus removes operator reading-error and decreases the analytical time because operator curve-reading or calculating is not necessary. Following Boling's lead, the Perkin–Elmer Corp. has developed a digitized, concentration readout which incorporates noise-suppression, scale expansion, and compensation for curvature of the analytical curve.

COMPLETE INSTRUMENTS

The detailed coverage of each presently available atomic absorption spectrometer is beyond the scope of this book. In addition, new manufacturers and new models are rapidly entering the market. For these reasons, discussions of only a few models will be given. More detailed information can be obtained from the manufacturers.

In North America, Perkin–Elmer, Jarrell–Ash, Beckman Instruments, and Evans Electroselenium produce commercially available instrumentation. The Westinghouse Corporation also manufactures a large variety of hollow cathode tubes. Overseas, at least Techtron, Zeiss, Unicam, and Hilger and Watts are manufacturing instrumentation. The instrumental statistics for several instruments are given in Table VIII (from KAHN, 1966). Examples of several commercial models are shown by the plates of this chapter (Fig.4–7).

Fig.4. Perkin–Elmer Model 303 atomic absorption spectrophotometer. (Published by courtesy of Perkin–Elmer Corp.)

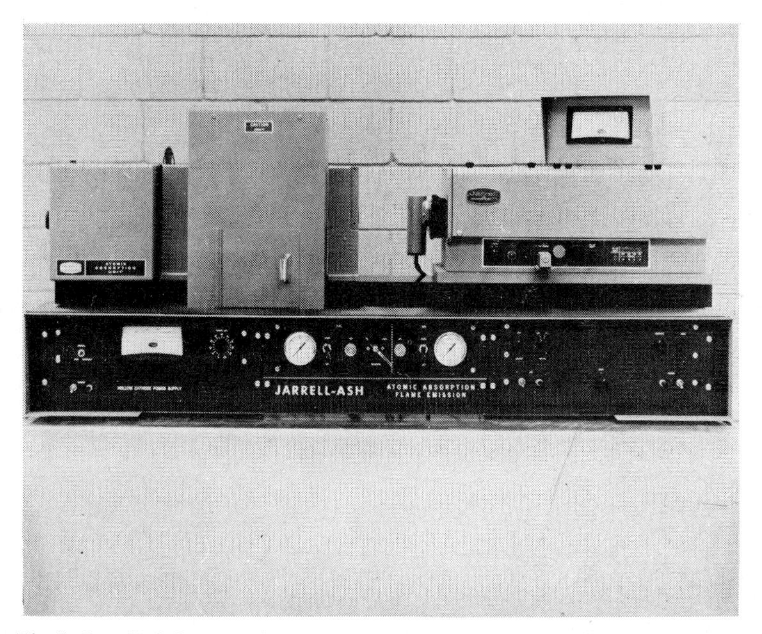

Fig.5. Jarrell–Ash Model 82–516 combination atomic absorption-flame emission unit. (Published by courtesy of Jarrell–Ash Co.)

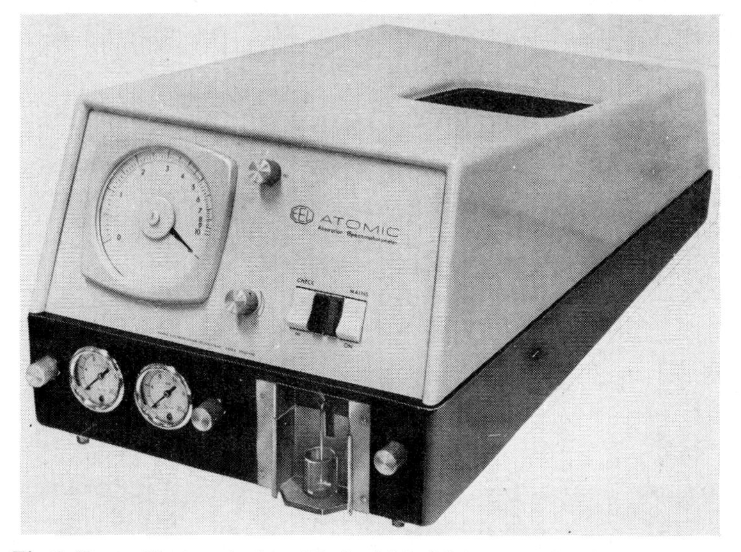

Fig.6. Evans Electroselenium Limited Model 140 atomic absorption unit (Published by courtesy of Evans Electroselenium Ltd.)

TABLE VIII

STATISTICS FOR DIFFERENT INSTRUMENTS[1]

Characteristic	*Beckman*		*Jarrell–Ash*	*Perkin–Elmer*		*Techtron*
	DU2	*DB*	*82-362*	*303*	*290*	*AA3*
Type of system	single beam d.c.	single beam a.c.	single beam a.c.	double beam a.c.	single beam a.c.	single beam a.c.
Burner (preferred)	3 total consumption	3 total consumption	1 total consumption	premix	premix	premix
Passes through flame	3	3	5	1	1	1
Monochromator	Littrow	Littrow	Ebert	Ebert	Littrow	Ebert
Disperser	prism	prism	grating	grating	grating	grating
Resolution (Å)	3UV 10 VIS	5UV 15 VIS	0.2	0.2	2	3.3
Mono focal length (mm)	500	260	500	400	267	500
Grating lines/mm	—	—	1,200	U.V. 2,880 VIS 1,400	1,800	600
Dispersion (Å/mm)	not given	not given	16	U.V. 6.5 VIS 13	16	33
Maximum bandpass (Å)	not given	not given	1.6	U.V. 20 VIS 40	20	10
Nominal wavelength range (mμ)	190–1000	205–700	not given	190–870	200–870	186–1000
Grating surface (mm)	—	—	52 × 52	64 × 64	64 × 64	50 × 50
Detector	1P28 and Red photo tube	1P28	1P28	EMI 9592B Bi–0–Ag	1P28 B	1P28
Standard readout	meter	meter	meter	counter	meter	meter
Linearity	% trans.	% trans.	% trans.	% absorption	concentration	% absorption
Scale expansion	no	no	no	1 ×, 2 ×, 5 × 10 ×	1 ×–4 ×	1 ×–5 ×
Readout accessory	recorder	recorder	recorder	digital concentration Readout, also recorder	recorder	recorder

Fig.7. Beckman Instruments Model 979 atomic absorption spectrophotometer. (Published by courtesy of Beckman Instruments Inc.)

METHODS OF INCREASING SENSITIVITY

Even though atomic absorption is quite sensitive, geochemists are constantly interested in increasing the sensitivity of any method. For this reason, some of the generally used methods are presented in this section.

Organic solvents

The improvement of sensitivity, by use of organic solvents, is the result of an increase in the amount of sample carried to the flame because of lower viscosity and of improved vaporization due to smaller droplet size resulting from the lower surface tension of the organic solvents. The most practical ketones used as organic solvents are acetone and 4-methyl-2-pentanone (Jarrell–Ash Report JO:RFJ, 1-66). Suitable alcohols are methanol, ethanol, and isopropanol.

ROBINSON (1961b) investigated the use of alcohol, acetone, benzene, and *n*-heptane as organic solvents for atomic absorption analysis. He demonstrated definite improvement over aqueous solutions for Ni, Zn, Co, Cu, Cd, Na, Ag, Mg, and Cr.

LOCKYER et al. (1961) demonstrated that a 50% v/v isopropanol solution increased absorption by Ni (2×), Cs (1.3×), Ag (2×), Ca (3×), Fe (8–10×), and Zn (2×) compared to aqueous solutions. ALLAN (1961) investigated a number of solvents miscible with water and reported the maximum sensitivity increase to be in 80% acetone solutions (factor of increase—3.5). He found identical results for Cu, Fe, Mn, Zn, and Mg. Using several solvents immiscible with water, he found an increase factor of sensitivity of up to 7.3 for ethyl-acetate. The results of ethyl-acetate were similar for Cu, Zn, Mn, and Fe.

Organic extraction

Silver has been concentrated by extraction with di-n-butylammonium into methyl isobutyl ketone (BELCHER et. al., 1964). Sensitivity was increased both by concentration into a smaller amount of fluid and by the four-fold increase in nebulization afforded by the organic solvent.

LAKANEN (1962) has extracted Bi, Cd, Co, Cu, Ga, In, Fe, Pb, Mn, Hg, Mo, Ni, Pd, Ag, Tl, Sn, V, and Zn from solutions at a pH of 5.0 ± 0.3. The compound used was pyrrolidine dithiocarbamic acid (PDTCH) extracted into chloroform. Atomic absorption analysis of chloroform solutions is difficult but another organic solvent for PDTCH can probably be found.

The use of ammonium pyrrolidine dithiocarbamate (APDC), extracted into methyl isobutyl ketone, or other organic solvents, as an effective concentration mechanism has been well established (SLAVIN, 1964b; SPRAGUE and SLAVIN, 1964; MANSELL and EMMEL, 1965). For example, WILLIS (1962) applied solvent extraction of ammonium pyrrolidine dithiocarbamate into methyl-n-amyl ketone to the determination of Pb, Hg, Bi, and Ni in urine. This concentration procedure allowed him to detect less than 1 mg/l of these elements. Elements which have been extracted with APDC include Cr, V, Mo, Mn, Cu, Zn, Pb, Bi, Hg, Ni, Sb, Cd, Fe, and Co.

Co-precipitation

BURRELL (1965) has coupled co-precipitation with organic extraction in the determination of Ni and Co in natural waters. The Ni and Co was co-precipitated with $Fe(OH_3)$, the precipitate acidized to a pH of 2.5 and exchanged with APDC in methyl isobutyl ketone after Fe removal. He was able to detect Ni at 0.3 p.p.b. and Co at 0.15 p.p.b. in the original sample. Similar methods hold great promise for hydrochemists.

Electronic methods

Electronic scale expansion of the absorbance signal was originally used by DAVID (1961) to achieve a five-fold expansion of low absorbances and the required electronics are now available on several commerical spectrometers.

Sensitivity can also be improved by judicious selection of the instrumental parameters. Each component of the instrument should be tested for maximum performance. That is, each analyst should test every element, using pure standard solutions, for the optimum lamp current, slit width, burner position, amplification, and fuel mixtures.

CHAPTER 4

Interferences

Compared to other spectral methods, atomic absorption spectrometry is relatively free from interferences, however certain interferences do exist. In this chapter, we shall first discuss the general types of interference and then discuss interferences pertinent to the determination of specific elements. By examining the specific interference tests given in later sections and with a knowledge of the major element composition of the sample, the analyst can predict possible interferences in his individual analyses.

SPECTRAL INTERFERENCE

This type of interference can be particularly troublesome to geochemists because most of their samples include a large number of elements. In a flame, light is emitted not only by the element being determined but also by the flame and by any other element present. If the spectral lines of any element cannot be resolved from those of the element being determined, a positive analytical error results because of the addition of the two signals. For example, in flame photometry the magnesium line (2852.1 Å) suffers interference by overlap from the 2852.8 Å line of sodium. The problem is essentially one of resolving the two lines, which requires an exceptionally fine monochromator.

However, in atomic absorption, the only absorption generally measured is that of the resonance line, with a width of ca. 0.01 Å. Thus the resolution is far better than in most emission methods and results in greatly increased freedom from spectral interference. The use of a modulated light source avoids the difficulty of measuring the emission of the element being determined which, if unmodulated, would decrease the absorption signal. A special type of spectral interference, herein called molecular absorption, will be discussed in a later section of this chapter.

It should be emphasized, however, that spectral interference can occur when using multielement hollow cathode tubes (JAWOROWSKI and WEBERLING, 1966). In these, other elements may emit radiation near the wavelength of the particular element under study. As these authors noted, even "single element" hollow cathode tubes may contain impurities in the cathode materials and thus act as multielement tubes. If multielement tubes are being used, the possibility of spectral interference should be investigated.

IONIZATION INTERFERENCE

Because of their low ionization potentials, the alkali metals more readily ionize than do other metals even in low temperature flames (Table IX). Ionization results in a smaller number of the atoms remaining in the ground state suitable for atomic absorption measurement. If another element is present which can supply free electrons, there is an increase in the number of ions returned to the ground state. The result is a positive error or increase in the ab-

TABLE IX

PERCENT IONIZATION OF ALKALI METALS[1]

Element	*Ionization potential e.v.*	*Air-propane 2,200°K*
Lithium	5.37	0.01
Sodium	5.12	0.3
Potassium	4.32	2.5
Rubidium	4.16	13.5
Cesium	3.87	28.3

[1] Reproduced from DEAN (1960), by permission of McGraw-Hill Book Co., Inc.

sorption because of the increased number of ground state atoms. Although this type of interference is most serious in the determination of alkali metals, it also occurs with alkaline earth metals (DICKSON and JOHNSON, 1966).

The effect is less pronounced in atomic absorption than in flame photometry (WILLIS, 1963). The problem can generally be negated by use of a standard-addition method (BILLINGS, 1965b) or by adding a large excess of the interfering element to both samples and standards. Such a "radiation buffer" is less objectionable in atomic absorption than in flame photometry because of less background and spectral interference from the introduced material.

CHEMICAL INTERFERENCE

An important type of interference occurring in both flame photometry and atomic absorption results from chemical combination of the element of interest with other elements or compounds. If this combination does not break down in the flame to produce ground state atoms, the result is a negative error in absorption or perhaps no absorption at all. The alkaline earths are particularly troublesome in this respect; forming compounds with aluminum, phosphorus, or silicon.

Two methods are used to overcome chemical interference. In the first, a large excess of a metal is added which can compete with the metal being determined for combination with the interfering element. This method presumably depends on the formation of a more stable or higher melting-point compound with the interfering element thus releasing the metal to be determined.

The second method consists of adding a large excess of a chelating compound such as EDTA. The improvement with the second method is thought to depend on a physical mechanism (BAKER and GARTON, 1961). Examples of the use of "chemical buffers" are discussed under specific elements.

Another type of chemical interference is shown by certain elements which tend to form refractory oxides in the flame, e.g.,

Al, Si, Be, B and to a lesser degree, Ca and Ba. This interference may be alleviated by the use of special burners and fuels as discussed in the chapter on instrumentation. MANNING (1966) shows that several of the chemical interferences reported when using low temperature flames (air–H_2) are not found with a nitrous oxide–acetylene flame.

MOLECULAR ABSORPTION

This type of spectral interference can be particularly troublesome to geochemists who often wish to determine trace elements in solutions of high-salt content. The interfering elements, of which Ca seems the most effective (WILLIS, 1963; BILLINGS, 1965a), block or absorb some of the light passing through the flame. The result is a positive error in the absorption measurement. For example, 18 percent absorption on the Zn line was caused by a 10,000 mg/l Spec-Pure Ca solution which contained no Zn (BILLINGS, 1965a).

This interference was first noted by the Australian spectroscopists ALLAN (1961a) and DAVID (1961). BILLINGS (1965a) made a detailed examination of the problem. He found a number of specific interferences which will be discussed in later sections.

Initially, the phenomenon was explained by assuming that particles of salt in the flame were impeding the light, hence the term "light scattering." BILLINGS (1963) proposed that a Ca-molecular absorption was interfering with Ba but presented no data to support his hypothesis. In his later work (BILLINGS, 1965a) he reverted to the term "light scattering" and explained the interferences as resulting from particulate matter. KOIRTYOHANN and PICKETT (1965a, b, 1966a, b) have demonstrated that many of the interferences termed "light scattering" are actually the result of molecular absorption by such species as SrO and CaOH. In addition, they have been unable to demonstrate light scattering by particulate matter in normal flames. KOIRTYOHANN and PICKETT (1966b) have demonstrated mathematically that the amount of absorbance on various wavelengths, as presented by BILLINGS (1965a), is too large to be the result of light scattering by particles.

S. R. Koirtyohann (personal communication, 1966) has suggested that the term "light scattering" is in error and should only be used in proven cases. The present authors agree with this and, because of the above evidence, use the term molecular absorption to indicate this type of spectral interference. The seriousness of the effect generally increases with decreasing wavelength, with increasing molarity of the major elements, and is dependent on flame parameters. With the exceptions of Ba, Cd, and Zn, satisfactory corrections can be made by measuring the molecular absorption effect on a nonabsorbing line very close to the resonance line. An alternative method is to prepare pure interference standards without the element to be determined, measure these on the resonance line, and, knowing the amount of interfering element in the sample, subtract its equivalent signal from the total signal. This method can also be used if more than one interfering element is present, as BILLINGS (1965a) has demonstrated the interferences are additive. Standard-addition methods are not effective in negating molecular absorption interferences because the same amount of signal is added to both sample and spiked-sample. KOIRTYOHANN and PICKETT (1965b) have suggested the use of a hydrogen lamp and a spectral line near the analyzing line to correct for molecular absorption. This method would be especially useful for Ba, Cd, and Zn (see BILLINGS, 1965a). As discussed in Chapter 3, high temperature flames reduce molecular absorption.

SPECIFIC ELEMENT INTERFERENCES

Aluminum

MANNING (1964) determined Al in a number of NBS metal-alloy standards. He found chemical interferences from large concentrations of Zn, Ca, Cu, and Fe and suggested that for maximum accuracy standards should closely match samples in chemical composition. Since Al interferes with the alkaline earths by chemical combination, it should be suspected that large amounts of the alkaline earths will interfere by the same process with Al.

Antimony

Little data on detailed atomic absorption procedures for the determination of antimony are available. MOSTYN and CUNNINGHAM (1967) determined Sb in various types of nonferrous alloys. They studied the possible interference on Sb absorption of (using the 2,175 Å line) a 100 p.p.m. Sb (in 2 *N* HCl) solution plus 1,000 p.p.m. of Al, Ba, Ca, Cd, Cr, Cu, Fe, K, Mg, Mn, Mo, Na, Pb, Sr, and Zn. Of these, only Cu showed a small interference at the Sb, 2,175.8 Å line. No suggestion of significant interference was indicated by any of the other metals tested.

Barium

To the authors' knowledge, the only interference studied for Ba has been molecular absorption (BILLINGS, 1963, 1965a; CAPACHO-DELGADO and SPRAGUE, 1965; KOIRTYOHANN and PICKETT, 1965a). Barium would be expected to chemically combine with Al, PO_4, and Si as do the other alkaline earths. P. C. Ragland (personal communication, 1966) has found an Al interference on Ba. Because of its low ionization potential, Ba should have an ionization interference from other alkaline earths and from the alkalis. Such ionization interference has been reported for K in the high temperature N_2O–C_2H_2 flame (SLAVIN et al. 1966).

Bismuth

BILLINGS (1965a) demonstrated molecular absorption on the Bi line (2,231 Å) by Ca, Mg, Na, and K in an air-propane flame. No other interference studies are known to the authors.

Cadmium

WILSON (1965) found no effect on Cd absorbance in solutions with the following cation ratios: Cr/Cd = 1000; Ni/Cd = 1000; Mn/Cd = 1000; Co/Cd = 500; Cu/Cd = 500; Mo/Cd = 250; Ti/Cd = 250; V/Cd = 250; Pb/Cd = 250; or Al/Cd = 250. He found a molecular absorption interference of Fe on the Cd 2,288 Å lines. Wilson was able to correct this by measurement of the absorption effect on the nonresonance line (2,321.2 Å). BILLINGS (1965a) demonstrated molecular absorption by Ca, Mg, Na, K, and Fe on the 2,288 Å line. He did not use a 2,321.2 Å line as a nonresonance line and was unable to correct for molecular absorption on any other nonresonance line.

SPRAGUE (1963) reported no interferences with the determination of Cd in Zn-alloy. PULIDO et al. (1966) reported molecular absorption by a 0.01 *M* NaCl solution. They also reported depression by 0.1 *M* H_3PO_4. No interference was found by 100 mg/l chloride salt solutions of Ba, Ca, Co, Cr, Cu, Fe, Li, Mg, Mn or Ni. Tenth molar solutions of HNO_3 or H_2SO_4 caused no interference; nor did 0.64 molar $HClO_4$.

Calcium

The interference of sulfate, phosphate, alumina, or silica on the determination of Ca has been reported by a number of authors (DAVID, 1959, 1960; WILLIS, 1960a, 1961; SPRAGUE, 1963; TRENT and SLAVIN, 1964b; JONES, 1965; PLATTE and MARCY, 1965; FISHMAN and DOWNS, 1966). This is an example of chemical interference as, apparently, a Ca–Al or Ca–Si complex is formed. The Ca is released by the addition of large amounts of La or Sr and a Ca analysis can then be made (WILLIS, 1961; BILLINGS, 1963). No molecular absorption effect has been noted on the Ca line (4227 Å) (BILLINGS, 1965).

In an investigation of water samples, PLATTE and MARCY (1965) report no interference on 1 p.p.m. Ca by 1,000 p.p.m. of Cl, NO_3,

NO_2, HCO_3, EDTA, Fe, Ni, Zn, Mn, Cr, B, Pb, Mg, or Na. For natural water samples, FISHMAN and DOWNS (1966) report low Ca values in basic solutions (pH > 7) or in the presence of more than 1,000 p.p.m. Mg. They report that 500 p.p.m. each of Na, K, and NO_3 cause no interference. Using a total consumption burner and an H_2-air flame, GALLE and ANGINO (1967) demonstrated serious interference by nitrate. As other workers have not found this interference, this may be another example of varying results due to different fuels and burners. Galle and Angino also reported that the type of acid used to dissolve the $CaCO_3$ affected the absorption. BILLINGS and HARRISS (1965) found no interferences on the determination of Ca in sea water. In a study of natural waters, BUTLER and BRINK (1963) report interferences on 16 p.p.m. Ca by 2,500 p.p.m. Mg or Na, 250 p.p.m. K, 10 p.p.m. PO_4, or 30 p.p.m. Al. The interferences were eliminated or considerably lessened by addition of 1,500 p.p.m. Sr. It is not known why there is a discrepancy in reported interferences on Ca, except that interferences can be a function of instrumental characteristics, especially flame parameters, therefore the analyst should make his own interference tests particularly with regard to anion interference. In natural waters the interference may also be a function of pH.

DAVID (1960) reports no interference on 8 p.p.m. Ca by 400 p.p.m. HCO_3. A depression effect by Be was noted by DAVID (1959). In his 1959 paper, David also reported enhancement of Ca absorption by either Na or K. This is probably an ionization interference and has also been reported by WILLIS (1960a). Ca has been determined in silicates by BILLINGS (1963) and by TRENT and SLAVIN (1964b). The only interferences were by Al and Si. The determination of Ca in carbonates is interference-free. DICKSON and JOHNSON (1966) have made a detailed investigation of interferences associated with Ca determination.

Cesium

BILLINGS (1965a) found no molecular absorption interference

on the Cs line (8,521 Å) in an air-propane flame. Ionization interferences would be expected in the presence of other alkalies.

Chromium

Ratios of Ni/Cr = 1,000, Mn/Cr = 1,000, Co/Cr = 1,000, Cu/Cr = 1,000, W/Cr = 1,000, Al/Cr = 400, V/Cr = 400, and Mo/Cr = 200 in alloys and steel produced no interferences on the absorbance of Cr (KINSON et al., 1963), however iron is a serious depressent. This effect can be reduced by the addition of ammonium chloride (BARNES, 1966). No evidence of molecular absorption interference with chromium was found by BILLINGS (1965a) using an air-acetylene flame.

In an investigation of water samples, PLATTE and MARCY (1965) found no interference on 1 p.p.m. Cr by 1,000 p.p.m. of SO_4, Cl, PO_4, NO_3, NO_2, HCO_3, Si, EDTA, Fe, Ni, Zn, Mn, B, Pb, Ca, Mg, or Na. The determination of Cr in carbonates is interference-free (G. K. Billings, unpublished data). P. C. Ragland (personal communication, 1966) has found that the accuracy of Cr determinations may be affected by pH of the solution.

Cobalt

In the analysis of steels, MCPHERSON (1963) found no interference from 20 weight % of Ni, Cr, or W; 10 weight % of Mo or Cu; 5 weight % of Si; 2 weight % of Mn or V; 1 weight % of Ti; or 0.5 weight % of S or P. BILLINGS (1965a), using an air-propane flame, reported molecular absorption on the Co line (2,407 Å) by Ca, Mg, K, and Na. The interference could be corrected using the nonresonance lines 2,383.4 Å or 2,389.5 Å. MCPHERSON et al. (1963) have reported molecular absorption interference by Fe. The determination of Co in carbonates is affected only by Ca molecular absorption (G. K. Billings, unpublished data). The determination of Co in silicates is generally interference-free (BILLINGS, 1963; BILLINGS and ADAMS (1964).

However, if the molarity of major elements is sufficiently high in the sample solution, molecular absorption can occur.

Copper

Molecular absorption is caused by Ca, Na, K and Mg on the Cu 3,247 Å line (BILLINGS, 1965) in an air-propane flame. A suitable correction can be made from the 2,961.1 Å line. WILSON (1964a) found no effect on the absorbance of 100 mg/l Cu by 500 mg/l Zn, 250 mg/l Mg or 50 mg/l Ag. KINSON and BELCHER (1964) report no interference on the determination of Cu in iron and steel by 20% Ni, Cr, Mn, or W; 10% Co or V; 5% Mo; or 1% Al (as weight % of solid).

PLATTE and MARCY (1965) found no interference on 1 p.p.m. Cu by 1,000 p.p.m. of SO_4, Cl, PO_4, NO_3, NO_2, HCO_3, Si, EDTA, Fe, Ni, Zn, Mn, Cr, B, Pb, Ca, Mg, or Na. FISHMAN and DOWNS (1966) reported that cations and anions normally found in natural waters do not interfere in the determination of Cu.

DAVID (1958) reported no interference on 2 p.p.m. Cu by 7,800 p.p.m. Na, 10,000 p.p.m. K, 3,000 p.p.m. Mg, 4,000 p.p.m. P, 1,000 p.p.m. S, or 120 p.p.m. Al. Increasing amounts of H_2SO_4 resulted in a decrease in absorbance, which may have been a viscosity effect. STRASHEIM et al. (1960) found no interference on Cu analysis by 10,000 p.p.m. Ca, Na, K, Al, or Co, 5,000 p.p.m. Fe, 1 N H_2SO_4, or 1 N HCl.

BELT (1964) reported that the amounts of Na, K, or Ca normally found in silicate rocks do not interfere with the determination of Cu. The determination of Cu in carbonates is only affected by Ca molecular absorption (Billings, unpublished data).

Gallium

MULFORD (1966) tested solutions containing 50 p.p.m. Ga and 5,000 p.p.m. of each of the following materials; Al, Mg, Cu, Zn, Cl, NO_3, PO_4, and SO_4. Only Al definitely interfered.

Gold

LOCKYER and HAMES (1959) report no interference from Pt, Pd, Rh, Fe, or Pb in the determination of Au; as was also reported by STRASHEIM and WESSELS (1963). PRICE and RAGLAND (1966a) report molecular absorption by Ca and/or Fe on Au.

Indium

MULFORD (1966) tested 50 p.p.m. in solutions by adding 5,000 p.p.m. each of : Al, Mg, Cu, Zn, Cl, NO_3, PO_4, and SO_4. Each of these interferents produced a reduction of the percent recovery.

Iron

ALLAN (1959) found no interference from 10 p.p.m. Mn, 3,000 p.p.m. K, 3,000 p.p.m. Ca, 1,000 p.p.m. Na, 1,000 p.p.m. Mg, or 500 p.p.m. P on a 10 p.p.m. solution of Fe. Two ml of 72% perchloric acid in 20 ml of solution produced no effect, whereas 5 ml of 72% perchloric acid increased the viscosity sufficiently to reduce the apparent Fe concentration by 7–8%. Ratios of Co/Fe = 100 and W/Fe = 500 apparently cause no interference with Fe determinations (BELCHER, 1963). DAVID (1958) reported no interference on 20 p.p.m. of Fe by 7,800 p.p.m. Na, 10,000 p.p.m. K, 8,000 p.p.m. Ca, 3,000 p.p.m. Mg, 4,000 p.p.m. P, 1,000 p.p.m. S, or 120 p.p.m. Al. He reported a decrease in absorbance with increasing content of H_2SO_4 which may have been a viscosity effect. BILLINGS (1965a) has demonstrated molecular absorption by Ca on the Fe line (2,483 Å) and possibly by Mg and Na, using an air-acetylene flame. The interfering absorption could be measured on the non-absorbing line (2,510.8 Å).

Silica interferes in the determination of Fe in natural waters (PLATTE and MARCY, 1965) but the interference is eliminated by the addition of Ca. PLATTE and MARCY (1965) report no interference on 1 p.p.m. Fe in water samples by 1,000 p.p.m. of sulfate, chloride, phosphate, nitrate, nitrite, bicarbonate, EDTA, Ni, Zn, Mn, Cr, B, Pb, Ca, Mg, or Na.

No interferences with Fe determination in cement were reported by SPRAGUE (1963) nor in silicate rocks (TRENT and SLAVIN, 1964a; BILLINGS and ADAMS, 1964; BILLINGS 1963). The determination of Fe in carbonates is affected only by Ca molecular absorption (G. K. Billings, unpublished data). No interferences with Fe determination in Fe-rich recent marine sediments were found by E. E. Angino and J. Watson (unpublished data).

Lead

DAGNALL and WEST (1964) made an extensive study of interferences in the determination of Pb. The cations investigated, in a 1,000-fold excess over Pb, were: Ag, Al, Ba, Be, Bi, Cd, Ce, Co, Cr, Cu, Fe, Hg, K, La, Li, Mg, Mn, Na, Ni, Sn, Sr, Tl, Th, Zn, and Zr. Be caused a precipitate: Al, Th and Zr interfered, presumably by the formation of a refractory compound. A 1,000-fold excess of each of the following anions was also studied: $B_4O_7^{2-}$, Br^-, Cl^-, ClO_3^-, Cn^-, SCN^-, CO_3^{2-}, ClO_4^-, CrO_4^{2-}, $Cr_2O_7^{2-}$, F^-, $Fe(CN)_6^{3-}$, $Fe(CN)_6^{4-}$, I^-, IO_3^-, MoO_4^{2-}, NO_2^-, NO_3^-, PO_4^{3-}, S^{2-}, SO_4^{2-}, $S_2O_3^{2-}$, $S_2O_8^{2-}$, VO_3^-, and WO_4^{2-}. Several anions produced precipitates, however, the addition of EDTA eliminated this problem. PO_4^{3-} and $S_2O_8^{2-}$ interfered slightly. MCPHERSON (1963) reports negligible interferences from 1 weight % of Ni, Cr, Mo; or Si; or from 2 weight % Mn. ROBINSON (1961a) found no interference from interferent/Pb ratios of 90, using the following metals; Sn, Na, Bi, Cu, Zn, Cr, Fe, or Ni.

BILLINGS (1965a) observed molecular absorption on the Pb line (2,170 Å) by Ca, Mg, K, and Na. The interference can be corrected by use of the 2,203.5 Å nonresonance line. Molecular absorption by $Ca_2(PO_4)_2$ was also noted by STRASHEIM et al. (1964).

Lithium

FISHMAN and DOWNS (1966) in an investigation of natural waters, found no interference on Li determination by 1,000 p.p.m. Na, 100 p.p.m. K, 200 p.p.m. Mg, 200 p.p.m. Ca, 1,500 p.p.m. Cl, 2,000 p.p.m. SO_4, or 100 p.p.m. NO_3. They report that Sr, at concentrations greater than 5 p.p.m., interferes. The Sr interference was not found by ANGINO and BILLINGS (1966) or by ZAIDEL and KORENNOI (1961). No definite molecular absorption was found by BILLINGS (1965a). The determination of Li in carbonates is interference-free (G. K. Billings, unpublished data).

Magnesium

As with the other alkaline earths, chemical interference from Al, Si, P, and sulfate is present in the determination of Mg (DAVID, 1960; WILLIS, 1961; PLATTE and MARCY, 1965; JONES, 1965; FISHMAN and DOWNS, 1966). These chemical interferences may be eliminated by the addition of a La, Sr or Ni buffer (DAVID, 1960; WILLIS, 1961; ANDREW and NICHOLS, 1962).

WILSON (1964a) observed no effect on the absorbance of 50 mg/l Mg by 200 mg/l Cu, 500 mg/l Zn, or 50 mg/l Ag. Using an interference buffer of 1,500 p.p.m. Sr in the final solution, no interference from 0.5 weight % P, Ti, or Zr; 1 weight % Zn; 2 weight % Al, V, Mn, or Si; 5 weight % Ni, Cu, or Mo; or from 10 weight % Cr, was found on 0.01 weight % Mg in iron (BELCHER and BRAY, 1961). DAVID (1960) found no interference on 4 p.p.m. Mg by 400 p.p.m. HCO_3^-, BILLINGS (1965a) found no evidence of molecular absorption in the determination of Mg.

PLATTE and MARCY (1965) report no interference on 1 p.p.m. Mg by 1,000 p.p.m. of Cl, NO_3, NO_2, HCO_3, EDTA, Fe, Ni, Zn, Mn, Cr, B, Pb, Ca, or Na. In their report of methods for water analysis, FISHMAN and DOWNS (1966) found that low values of Mg result if the sample pH is above 7. They also report no interference from 400 p.p.m. each of Na, K, and Ca, nor from 2 p.p.m. Zn. BILLINGS and HARRISS (1965) found no interferences with the determination of Mg in sea water. GALLE and ANGINO (1967), using an H_2-air flame, reported nitrate interference with the Mg absorption.

WILLIS (1960b) investigated Mg in blood serum and reported a complexing interference by protein which could be overcome by addition of 10,000 p.p.m. EDTA or by 1,500 p.p.m. Sr. The only interferences affecting Mg determination in silicates are those discussed in the first paragraph of this section (BILLINGS, 1963; RAGLAND and BILLINGS, 1965). The determination of Mg in carbonates is interference-free (G. K. Billings, unpublished data).

Manganese

ALLAN (1959) found no interference on a 10 p.p.m. Mn solution by 10 p.p.m. Fe, 500 p.p.m. P, 1,000 p.p.m. Mg, 1,000 p.p.m. Na, 3,000 p.p.m. Ca, or 3,000 p.p.m. K. Five ml of 72% perchloric acid in a 20 ml solution of sample decreased the aspiration rate sufficiently to cause a 7–8% reduction in the apparent Mn concentration. BILLINGS (1965a) demonstrated molecular absorption by Ca, Mg, and possibly by Na or K, using an air-propane flame. The interference correction could be measured on the 2,576.1 Å Mn line.

BELCHER and KINSON (1964) reported that 20% Cr (weight % of solid) caused enhancement equivalent to 10% of the Mn in the solution. This may be another example of molecular absorption that has not been tested. In their investigation, no interference was found from 30% Ni; 10% W or Co; 5% Mo or Cu; 3% Si; 2% V; or 0.5% Al (as weight % of solid). No measurable effect occurred from 10,000 p.p.m. Fe in the solution. A 10% v/v HCl,H_2SO_4, or H_3PO_4 caused a slight depression of the signal, which may be the result of a reduced aspiration rate.

Silica interferes with the determination of Mn, presumably by the formation of complex ions or colloidal silicates (PLATTE and MARCY, 1965). The interference can be eliminated by adding Ca. Platte and Marcy also found no interference on 1 p.p.m. Mn by 1,000 p.p.m. of SO_4, Cl, PO_4, NO_3, NO_2, HCO_3, EDTA, Fe, Ni, Zn, Cr, B, Pb, Ca, Mg, or Na. FISHMAN and DOWNS (1966) report that cations and anions normally found in natural waters do not interfere in the determination of Mn. The determination of Mn in carbonates is affected only by Ca molecular absorption (G. K. Billings, unpublished data); E. E. Angino and J. Watson (unpublished data) found no interferences with Mn determination in recent marine sediments.

Molybdenum

MOSTYN and CUNNINGHAM (1966) have investigated the likely interferences during the determination of Mo in ferrous alloys. Iron addition leads first to a depression of absorbance, but with increasing amounts an enhancement is apparent at 3,000 p.p.m. Fe. The latter effect is possibly molecular absorption. The addition of Mn also interfered. Al and NO_3^-, in combination, caused severe depression of the absorbance. The Mn and Fe interference could be eliminated by neutralization with NH_4Cl, which was less effective in the presence of Al and NO_3. The latter combination did not overcome the Mn or Fe interference. BILLINGS (1965a) found no molecular absorption from Na, Ca, Mg, or K. In analyses of recent marine sediments, E. E. Angino and M. Baird (unpublished data) found no interferences with Mo determination other than Ca.

In a detailed study of Mo, DAVID (1961) found little interference on 10 p.p.m. Mo by 500 p.p.m. of Zn, K, Al, Cl, Si, P, Cr, Ni, or Na. He reported suppressive interference from 500 p.p.m. Mn, Ca, Sr, or Fe; and slight interference from Mg or Sr. David found that the addition of 1,000 p.p.m. Al completely suppressed the effect of 500 p.p.m. of the interfering element.

Nickel

The presence of 30% Cr; 20% Mn or W; 10% Cu or Co; and 5% V, Mo, or Al (as weight % of solid) produced no interference on the determination of Ni in iron and steel (KINSON, 1964). BILLINGS (1965a) reported molecular absorption by Ca on the Ni line (2,320 Å) in an air-acetylene flame. Correction for molecular absorption could be made on the 2,325.7 Å Ni line. P. C. Ragland (personal communication, 1966) has found molecular absorption by Ca and/or Fe in the analysis of granites.

In an investigation of water samples, PLATTE and MARCY (1965) found no interference on 1 p.p.m. Ni by 1,000 p.p.m. of SO_4, Cl, PO_4, NO_3, NO_2, HCO_3, Si, EDTA, Fe, Zn, Mn, Cr, B, Pb, Ca, Mg, or Na. The determination of Ni in carbonates is affected only by Ca molecular absorption (G. K. Billings, unpublished data). The determination of Ni in silicates is relatively interference-free providing that the Ca or Fe content is not large enough to cause molecular absorption, (BILLINGS and ADAMS, 1964; RAGLAND and BILLINGS, 1965).

Palladium

LOCKYER and HAMES (1959) reported no interference from Au, Pt, Rh, Fe, or Pb on the determination of Pd; as was also noted by STRASHEIM and WESSELS (1963).

Platinum

LOCKYER and HAMES (1959) reported no interference on Pt determination by Au, Pd, Rh, Fe, or Pb. In a more recent investigation, interference with the determination of Pt has been reported for Pd (125 p.p.m.), Rh (5 p.p.m.), Au (80 p.p.m.), Ir (5 p.p.m.), Ru (5 p.p.m.), Os (80 p.p.m.), or Na (5 p.p.m.) (STRASHEIM and WESSELS, 1963). These interferences could be overcome by the addition of 20,000 p.p.m. Cu.

Potassium

FISHMAN and DOWNS (1966) report that of the cations and anions in natural waters, only Na interferes. This is an ionization interference and has been noted by numerous authors (WILLIS, 1960c; TRENT and SLAVIN, 1964a; BILLINGS, 1965b). Ionization interference of Na on K determinations in sea water does occur but the effect can be eliminated by matching samples to standards, with regard to Na (BILLINGS and HARRISS, 1965).

The determination of K in carbonates is interference-free (G. K. Billings, unpublished data). The determination of K in silicates is quite accurate and is only affected by a Na ionization interference that can be eliminated by buffering when necessary (BILLINGS and ADAMS, 1964; BILLINGS, 1965c).

DAVID (1960) reports no interference with 4 p.p.m. K by 160 p.p.m. of P, Al, or S; nor by 64 p.p.m. of Si. No molecular absorption on the K line (7,665 Å) was reported by BILLINGS (1965a).

Rhodium

LOCKYER and HAMES (1959) reported no interference on Rh determination by Au, Pt, Pd, Fe, or Pb. In a more recent investigation, interference with Rh was evidenced by Na, Pt, Pd, Au, Ir, Ru, or Os (STRASHEIM and WESSELS, 1963).

Rubidium

An ionization interference by Na or K on Rb determinations has been reported by Slavin et al. (1965). The effect levels off with increasing Na or K concentration, which explains the lack of interference on Rb determination in sea water (BILLINGS and HARRISS, 1965). The determination of Rb in carbonates is interference-free (G. K. Billings, unpublished data). The determination of Rb in silicates is quite accurate and the ionization effect of Na or K, although serious, can be buffered if necessary (BILLINGS, 1965c). BILLINGS (1965a) found no molecular absorption on the Rb line (7,800 Å) in an air-propane flame.

Selenium

MANNING and SLAVIN (1964) report that in the determination of Se in Cu, a slight interference from Cu is present. This appeared to be a difference in the physical character of the high-Cu solutions and could be negated by using standards with a similar Cu content to that of the sample.

Silicon

As far as interferences for silicon are concerned, little information exists in the literature as a guide. Using the Jarrell–Ash triflame burner and a nitrous oxide–acetylene flame, O. K. Galle and E. E. Angino (unpublished data) find that 50 p.p.m. calcium interferes slightly over the range 50–200 p.p.m. SiO_2. Lithium in high concentrations (2,000 and 3,000 p.p.m.) causes some interferences on the determination of silica in the 10–100 p.p.m. range. Similar interferences were not found by W. Slavin and C. E. Mulford (personal communication, 1967) using a nitrous oxide burner and a Perkin–Elmer Model 303 atomic absorption unit. These differences may be due to differences in burner design.

Silver

WILSON (1964b) compared a series of aqueous Ag solutions to the same amount of Ag in 10% HNO_3 and found a 7% decrease in absorbance. Since the analytical curves were nearly parallel, this effect may have been the result of a decrease in aspiration rate rather than an interference. He found no effect from a 2% NaOH solution, but demonstrated an appreciable decrease in absorbance in solutions containing 5,000 mg/l Al. Wilson also found no effect of 500 mg/l of Zn, Mg, Cu, Mn, Cr, Ti, Fe, and Ni on the absorbance of 10 mg/l Ag.

BELCHER et al. (1964) have made a detailed study of possible interferences on the determination of Ag. They report no interferences of 1,000-fold mole excess (as nitrate) of: Al, Ba, Be, B, Ca, Cd, Ce^{3+}, Co, Cr, Cu^{2+}, Fe^{3+}, Hg^{2+}, K, La, Li, Mg, Mn^{2+}, Na, NH_4^+, Ni, Pb, Sn^{4+}, Sr, Tl^{1+}, Zn, and Zr. Thorium was found to reduce the signal approximately 15% presumably because of a refractory thorium oxide involving Ag. No interference was found from a 1,000-fold mole excess of the sodium, potassium or ammonium salts of $B_4O_7^{2-}$, Br^-, Cl^-, ClO_3^-, CN^-, Co_3^{2-}, CrO_4^{2-}, CrO_7^{2-}, $Fe(CN)_6^{3-}$, $Fe(CN)_6^{4-}$, I^-, MoO_4^{2-}, NO_2^-, NO_3^-, PO_4^{3-}, SCN^-, SO_4^{2-}, $S_2O_3^{2-}$, $S_2O_8^{2-}$, and VO_3^-. A 1,000-fold mole excess of the sodium or potassium salts of acetate, formate, oxalate, tartrate, phthalate, or citrate caused no interference. Possible interferences of hydrochloric, sulphuric, nitric, phosphosphoric, and acetic acid were investigated. No interference from HCl or HNO_3 occurred but sulphuric and phosphoric reduced the absorbance (ca. 20%) because of the increased viscosity. Acetic acid caused an enhancement of absorbance by acting as an organic solvent.

Sodium

Up to 3,000 p.p.m. K had no effect on Na absorption measured during a study of Na in limestones by RUBESKA et al. (1963). They reported that large variations of HCl, Cl, and Ca affected the slope of the curve by altering the release of Na in the flame. One of us (G. K. Billings) has likewise investigated Na in a $CaCO_3$ matrix and has found no spectral interferences. The determination of Na in silicates is generally interference-free (BILLINGS, 1963; BILLINGS and ADAMS, 1964).

A study of Na in phosphorus was made by PERKINS (1963). He found only slight interference on mg/l amounts of Na by a 1% Ca solution, by a 1% phosphate solution, or by a 1% Ca phosphate solution. ROBINSON (1960) found no ionization interference on 10 p.p.m. Na by 5,000 p.p.m. of K or Li. DAVID (1960) reported no interference on 2 p.p.m. Na by 160 p.p.m. P, Al, or S; nor by 64 p.p.m. Si. BUTLER and BRINK (1963) report a slight interference of 250 p.p.m. Cu on 4 p.p.m. Na. BILLINGS (1965a) found no molecular absorption on the Na line (5,890 Å) in an air-acetylene flame. None of the cations or anions in normal amounts in fresh water interfere with Na determinations (FISHMAN and DOWNS, 1966) nor in sea water (BILLINGS and HARRISS, 1965).

Strontium

Several investigators have reported a chemical interference of Al and P on Sr (DAVID, 1962; BILLINGS, 1963; BELCHER and BROOKS, 1963; TRENT and SLAVIN, 1964b; JONES, 1965). The interference of Al results from chemical combination with Sr and can be eradicated by buffering the solution with an excess of La (DAVID, 1960). The interference of P does not respond as well to La or other metal buffering (DAVID, 1962). BILLINGS (1965a) found no molecular absorption on the Sr line by Ca, Na, K, Mg, or Fe, in an air-acetylene flame.

BELCHER and BROOKS (1963) tested a 4 mg/l solution of Sr and found no interference from 300 mg/l Al, 50 mg/l PO_4^3, 300 mg/l Al, 10 mg/l PO_4^3, 20 mg/l Na, 20 mg/l K, 100 mg/l Fe, 100 mg/l Ca, 100 mg/l Mg, 2 mg/l Mn, 20 mg/l Ti, or 50% v/v acid changes.

FISHMAN and DOWNS (1966) have reported that an ionization interference is caused by Na and K on determination of Sr in fresh waters. This interference levels off above 100 p.p.m. of Na or K. The interference is automatically compensated for in brines and sea water because of the high Na Content (BILLINGS and HARRISS, 1965; BILLINGS and ANGINO, 1965; ANGINO et al., 1966). No interferences are found in the determination of Sr in carbonates and the analysis is quite accurate (BILLINGS, 1965c). Only the chemical interferences discussed above affect Sr determinations in silicates (BILLINGS, 1963; TRENT and SLAVIN, 1964b; BILLINGS and ADAMS, 1964).

Tellurium

MANNING and SLAVIN (1964) reported a slight interference during the analysis of Te in Cu. They propose that the depression was the result of physical differences between the high-Cu solutions and the standards and suggest matching the Cu content of both solutions.

Thallium

BILLINGS (1965a) found no molecular absorption on the Tl line (3,776 Å) in an air-acetylene flame.

Tin

Agazzi (1965) reported interferences on 0.6 mg/l Sn, in an H_2O_2 matrix, as follows: 500 mg/l $NaNO_3$ caused enhancement; 20 mg/l Na_3PO_4 or $Na_4P_2O_7$ caused depression of the absorbance. The depression was probably the result of chemical interference.

Zinc

Burrell (1965b) determined zinc in amphibolites and reported no interferences from solutions containing 5 p.p.m. Zn and up to 2,000 p.p.m. Ca. Iron produced a slight enhancement in concentrations greater than 100 p.p.m. Fe. Aluminum enhanced a 10 p.p.m. Zn signal at concentrations less than 100 p.p.m. Al but depressed above this value. $MgSO_4$ showed severe depression of the signal at concentrations above 10 p.p.m. whereas $MgNO_3$ had no effect.

The lack of Ca interference in Burrell's study is surprising in that Billings (1965a) demonstrated Ca molecular absorption at concentrations as low as 500 mg/l Ca. He also found molecular absorption exhibited by Na, K, Mg, and Fe on the Zn analytical line (2,138 Å). The discrepancy may be the result of fuel differences in the two studies. No satisfactory nonresonance line could be located for correction purposes.

Wilson (1963, 1964a) found no effect on a 100 mg/l Zn absorbance by 200 mg/l Cu, 250 mg/l Mg, Or 50 mg/l Ag. He found no anion interference on 1 mg/l Zn solutions containing 0.1 *N* chloride, sulphate, chromate, phosphate, or benzoate prepared as the A.R. sodium salt. Using a 50 p.p.m. Zn solution, Erdey et al. (1963) found essentially no interferences from 5/1 mole ratios of the following anions: Cl^1, NO_3^1, SO_4^{2-}, PO_4^{3-}, CH_3COO^-, BO_3^{3-}, I^-, or Br^-. The anions were introduced both as the acid and as the ammonium salt. They found only minor interferences from 10/1 weight ratio of Ag or Hg^2; 15/1 weight ratio Cr^3, Fe^3, Mn^2, Ni^2, or Bi^3; or from a 30/1 weight ratio of Cd, Co^2, or Cu^4.

In an investigation of water samples, Platte and Marcy (1965) found no interference on 1 p.p.m. Zn by 1,000 p.p.m. of SO_4, Cl, PO_4, NO_3, NO_2, HCO_3, Si, EDTA, Fe, Ni, Mn, Cr, B, Pb, Ca, Mg, or Na.

ALLAN (1961b) reported no variation in the absorbance value for 6 p.p.m. Zn in 0.5 *N* hydrochloric, sulphuric, nitric, or perchloric acid.

In an investigation of plant analysis by atomic absorption, DAVID (1958) found no interference on 1 p.p.m. Zn by 7,800 p.p.m. Na, 10,000 p.p.m. K, 8,000 p.p.m. Ca, 3,000 p.p.m. Mg, 4,000 p.p.m. S, or 120 p.p.m. Al. He reported a decrease in absorbance with increasing amounts of H_2SO_4 which may have resulted from increasing viscosity.

BELT (1964) has reported that the amounts of Na, K, Ca, P, or Cu normally found in silicate rocks do not interfere with the determination of Zn. However, numerous studies by the present authors and several others have clearly shown a serious molecular absorption interference with the determination of zinc. The determination of Zn in carbonates is affected only by Ca molecular absorption (G. K. Billings, unpublished data).

FUWA et al. (1964) found no interferences on 0.5 p.p.m. Zn by $10^{-3}M$ EDTA or O-phenanthroline. The presence of 0.05 *M* Na phosphate or 0.2% trichloro-acetic acid caused a depression of the absorbance of 0.26 p.p.m. Zn. A solution of 100 p.p.m. of Ba, Ca, Cp, Cr, Cu, Fe, Li, Mg, Mn, or Ni did not interfere with the absorbance of 0.2 mg/l Zn.

Untested elements

To the authors' knowledge, no interference tests have been made for the following elements: Be, B, Ge, Hg, Nb, the lathanides, He, Ar, Ne, Xe, Kr, Rh, Ru, Sc, Ti, W, U, or V.

The following list of reagents provides a guide to those reagents which provide some protection against interference.

APPENDIX TO CHAPTER 4

REAGENTS FOR PROTECTION AGAINST INTERFERENCE[1]

Reagent	*Type*	*Protects Against*	*Used Analyte*
1% Cs solution	Deionizer	Alkalis	K, Na, Pb
1% Na solution	Deionizer	Alkalis	Rb, Cs
1% K solution	Deionizer	Alkalis	Rb
1% Rb solution	Deionizer	Alkalis	Cs, Na
1% Ba solution	Deionizer	Alkalis	Na, K
1% Ca solution	Deionizer	Alkalis	Sr
1% Al $(NO_3)_3$	Buffer	Condensed phase	Li, Na, K
1% NH_4 citrate	Buffer	Condensed phase	Li, Rb, Co
$(NH_4)_2$ HPO_4	Buffer	Condensed phase	Na, K
CoCl	Volatilizer	Condensed phase	Na, K
K_2CO_3	Buffer	Cationic interference	Mg
EDTA	Protector	Condensed phase	Mg, Ca, Cr, Mn, Co, Cu
Na Cl	Deionizer	Complexes	Ca
Trichloroacetric acid	Protector	Condensed phase	Ca
Mg + $HClO_4$	Volatilizer	Alkalis	Ca
HF + butanol	Volatilizer	Condensed phase	Al
NH_4Cl	Volatilizer	Condensed phase	Al, Rare Earths, Mo
Ba	Releaser	Al, Fe	Na, K, Mg
Ca	Releaser	F, Al	Mg
Sr	Releaser	F, Al	Mg
Mg + HClO	Releaser	P, Al, Si, S	Ca
Sr + $HClO_4$	Releaser	Al, P, B	Ca, Mg, Ba
La	Releaser	P, Al, Si, S and their anions	Ca, Sr, Ba
Nd, Sm, Y	Releaser	P, Al, S	Ca, Sr
Ca	Releaser	P, Al	Sr
Nd, Pr	Releaser	P, Al, S	Sr
Mg + glycerol	Releaser	Al, Ti, Cr, Fe	Sr
NH_4 Cl	Protector	Al	Na
HF	Volatilizer	Oxides	Zr, Ti, W
HCl	Volatilizer	Oxides	Ta, V
NH_4 EDTA	Protector	P, Al, Si	Mg, Ca
Glycerol	Protector	P	Ca, Sr
Glycerol + $HClO_4$	Volatilizer	P, Al, Si, S	Ca, Mg, Sr, Li
Mannitol	Protector	Cr, Fe, Ti	Ca, Mg, Sr, Li
Oxine	Chelator	Al	Ca
Salicyclic acid	Protector	Al	Ca
Acetyl acetone	Protector	Al	Ca
Sucrose	Protector	P, B	Ca. Sr

[1] Courtesy Jarrell-Ash Company

PART II

Methods and Applications

CHAPTER 5

Hydrogeochemistry

The atomic absorption method is particularly well suited to the measurement of the metal content of natural waters of all types and for the study of stream pollution (BUTLER and BRINK, 1963). Since atomic absorption analysis generally requires that the metal be in solution, this requirement is met by the sample itself. Consequently, for some water samples little preparation is required. If the metal concentrations are below the sensitivity limits of any instrument, they can be raised by evaporation, ion exchange and/or liquid–liquid extraction techniques. As SLAVIN (1965) has pointed out "since the methods are so simple. . . its simplicity discourages formal publications".

For the purpose of discussion, we have arbitrarily set up a three fold classification of water types. These are fresh water, sea water, and brines. By the latter we mean a water whose ionic strength normally exceeds that of sea water.

FRESH WATER

In what was apparently the first large-scale application of the method, BUTLER and BRINK (1963) describe the application of atomic absorption methods to the analysis of calcium, magnesium, iron, sodium, potassium, and copper in river, borehole, and well-waters. All the samples were filtered to remove the suspended material. Owing to the extreme sensitivity of the atomic absorption method for some elements (e.g., Na, Mg), sample dilution was necessary when "high" concentrations of these elements were present. Subsequent to filtering, the samples were aspirated directly into an air-acetylene (Ca, Mg, Fe) or an air–propane–butane (Cu, K, Na) flame. Interferences were noted for calcium and magnesium, but these were overcome by the addition of 1,500 p.p.m. $SrCl_2$. A detailed discussion of these interferences has already been presented. In all analyses comparisons were made with standard solutions spanning the concentration ranges encountered.

Coefficients of variation, calculated on absorption values, ranged from 7.4% for Ca at the 1–4 p.p.m. level to 0.76% for Cu at the 16 p.p.m. level and 0.72% for Fe at the 8 p.p.m. level. Accuracy when compared with gravimetric and EDTA titration methods were adequate.

WHEAT (1964) described an evaluation of atomic absorption for determining iron, chromium, nickel, cobalt, manganese and copper in water at the p.p.b. level. Of these elements 2–50 p.p.b. in unfiltered water were determined with a 10-fold concentration (by evaporation) of a 100 ml sample. A multiple pass system was used with an O_2–H_2 flame for Fe and Cu and an O_2–C_2H_2 flame for the others. Coefficients of variation ranged from 3%, for Cu (0.1–10 p.p.m.) to 5% for Fe (2–200 p.p.m.).

Atomic absorption provides a more accurate and rapid means of analysis of trace elements in river, well, and lake water than by the time consuming wet chemical, gravimetric, volumetric or colorimetric methods. PLATTE and MARCY (1965) give results obtained

TABLE X

COMPARISON OF ATOMIC ABSORPTION AND COLORIMETRIC DETERMINATION OF TRACE METALS IN RIVER AND WELL WATER (P.P.M.)[1]

(Modified from PLATTE and MARCY, 1965)

Sample	*Fe*		*Cu*		*Mn*		*Ca*		*Mg–*	
	A.A.	*C*	*A.A.*	*C*	*A.A.*	*C*	*A.A.*	*C*	*A.A.*	*C*
River water	0.67	0.65	0.12	0.14						
Well water	3.87	3.82	0.76	0.74	1.60	1.59	18.7	19.0	4.8	4.7

[1] A.A. = atomic absorption; C = colorimetric. Reproduced by courtesy of Perkin–Elmer Corp.

from river and well waters (Table X) where the trace metal content for Fe, Cu, Mn, Ca, and Mg ranged from 0.12 p.p.m. Cu to 19.0 p.p.m. Ca. Their standards were made by dissolving reagent-grade salts of the metals in a solution containing 10 ml concentrated HCl (s.g.1.19)/l of deionized water. All water samples were acidified with HCl (1 ml concentrated HCl /100 ml sample) and autoclaved at 250°F to solubilize particulate matter. Thus the analyses give "total" metal values as no separation of dissolved and suspended material was obtained. With an air-acetylene flame phosphate and aluminum interferences were noted in the analyses of Ca and Mg but were eliminated by addition of lanthanum. Similarly silica interfered with the determination of Fe, Mn and Ca. Analyses of solutions containing 1 p.p.m. Fe, Cu, Ni, Zn, Mn, Cr, Ca, or Mg showed no interferences in the presence of 1,000 p.p.m. of sulfate, chloride, phosphate, nitrate, nitrite, bicarbonate, silica, EDTA, iron, nickel, zinc, manganese, chromium, boron, lead, calcium, magnesium or sodium. The precision and accuracy equaled, if not exceeded, that of standard wet chemical methods.

Since many metals are present in natural waters in the range of 1 p.p.b., the two-stage preconcentration technique described by BURRELL (1965a), for Ni and Co deserves mention as it can probably be applied to the analyses of other metals as well.

The technique is as follows: 10 l of filtered (0.45μ) water were acidified to pH 2.5 with HCl. Add 10 ml of 1 *M* $FeCl_3$ and raise the pH to 9.0 with NH_4OH. The supernatant is siphoned off and the above procedure repeated twice. Subsequent to centrifugation to remove the remaining water, the combined coprecipitate is taken up in 8 *M* HCl and the iron removed by several extractions with isopropyl ether. The solution is evaporated to dryness and taken up to 100 ml with HCl to give a final pH of 2.5. Ammonium pyrrolidine dithiocarbamate (APDC) is used as the chelating agent and methyl isobutyl ketone (MIBK) as the organic solvent. Working curves can be prepared by chelating and extracting pure standards. Optimum results were obtained by using 10 ml of 1% APDC, followed by a 10-fold concentration into MIBK. The method was developed for both river and ocean water.

G. E. Likens and F. H. Bormann (quoted in SLAVIN, 1965) have used atomic absorption for the analysis of calcium, magnesium, potassium, sodium, iron, manganese, strontium and lithium in lake waters with no sample preparation other than dilution where necessary. Similarly E. E. Angino and S. Schulz (unpublished data) and E. E. Angino and O. K. Galle (unpublished data) have used the technique for the analysis (0.01–1.0 p.p.m.) of calcium, strontium, manganese, nickel, cobalt, zinc, iron, magnesium, and lithium in small ponds and river waters. The only prior treatment was filtration. PRICE and RAGLAND (1966a) determined Na, K, Ca, Mg, Fe, Mn, Li, Sr, Zn, and Cu in ground water from the Piedmont Province of North Carolina. No interferences were noted. The samples were filtered and EDTA added to each sample. Sodium and K were checked by flame photometry. Agreement of results was good.

FISHMAN and DOWNS (1966) have developed methods for the rapid determination of Ca, Cu, Li, Mg, Mn, K, Na, Sr, and Zn in most natural waters. Interferences are minor (See Chapter 3 for details). The first step for all analyses is to filter the sample through 0.45μ micropore membrane filters. For Cu, Zn, Mn, and Li, Na and K, the filtrate can be aspirated directly into the flame. A simple direct method for the determination of cadmium in fresh water is given in RAMAKRISHNA et al. (1967). The method requires no prior concentration or treatment of sample. Few interferences were found and can be eliminated by addition of EDTA. Sensitivity is 2 p.p.b.

Prior to analysing for Ca and Mg, add 1.0 ml of $LaCl_3$–HCl solution to 10 ml of filtrate and then aspirate. Prepare the LaCl–HCl solution by dissolving 58.65 g of La_2O_3 slowly and in small amounts in 250 ml of concentrated HCl (the reaction is violent) and dilute to 500 ml. Strontium is handled similarly, except that a $LaCl_3$–KCl solution is used. Prepare this solution by dissolving 117.3 g La_2O_3 in a minimum amount of dilute HCl. Add 19.1 g of KCl and dilute to 1 l. The standard addition method should be used for the determination of Sr in highly mineralized water or brines. A fuel-rich flame is recommended for the determination of Ca, Mg and Sr. In the analysis of K a Na/K ratio of 1 in both samples and standards is advised (see Chapter 4). BUTLER and MATTHEWS (1966) describe a method for the determination of molybdenum in water samples with little preparation other than acidifying and partial concentration by evaporation. Evaporate 500 ml of sample to 40 ml and add 2 ml of HCl to dissolve any precipitate formed. Iron can be prevented from interfering by adding 5 ml of a 10% citric acid solution to complex the Fe. Adjust the pH to 2.0 and transfer the mixture to a separatory funnel and add 5 ml of a 2% APDC solution. Add 10 ml of *n*-amyl methyl ketone and after shaking the mixture, allow it to stand for 10 min to allow separation of the two phases. Discard the aqueous phase and place the organic phase containing the Mo in a beaker convenient for handling. This solution can be aspirated directly into an air–acetylene flame. Only Fe interferes significantly. The accuracy and precision of the method are satisfactory.

In analyses of distilled and fresh water, sensitivities and detection limits for many elements can be improved by a factor of 2–3 by using 80% methanol, rather than water as a solvent. Aqueous samples can be concentrated and then diluted with methanol to gain this sensitivity (WHEAT, 1965).

WHEAT (1965) reports a limnological study of biologically active elements in pond water to establish their vertical and seasonal variations. Ca, Mg, Na, K were determined directly. The elements Co, Cu, Fe, Mn, Sr, and Zn, were measured after 200× concentration. A 5-gallon sample of pond water was concentrated in a "Diamond" continuous water sample Evaporator and evaporated to dryness.

Dilute the filtrate to 100 ml and analyse directly by atomic absorption. Hydrogen peroxide and HNO_3 can be added during the concentration step to destroy any organic matter. Preconcentration of large samples (20–50 gallons) can easily bring many elements present in extremely low concentration to within a measurable range (WHEAT, 1965).

For the study of most trace metals in the concentration range 0.01–10 p.p.m. in fresh water, little if any prior treatment is required other than filtration. The latter step is necessary to assure that only the dissolved portion is being examined. It is this simplicity of sample preparation, together with the atomic absorption method, that has made this technique of analysis so popular in water studies. Methods for the preparation of standards for these studies can be obtained in any analytical chemistry book and often are available from the instrument manufacturers. Standards (commonly 1% solutions) can be purchased from several chemical supply houses.

Table XI lists some sensitivity values (for distilled water) which would probably be obtainable in most fresh water systems.

TABLE XI

REPORTED SENSITIVITIES FOR 1% ABSORPTION FOR SOME ELEMENTS IN DISTILLED WATER SOLUTIONS[1]

Element	*Sensitivity*	*Line Å*	*Fuel*
Ag	0.1	3,281	H_2
As	3.0	1,937	C_2H_2
Ba	5.0	5,536	C_2H_2
Ca	0.1	4,226	H_2
Cd	0.005	2,288	H_2
Co	0.1	2,407	H_2
Cr	0.2	3,579	H_2
Cu	0.03	3,247	H_2
Fe	0.1	2,483	H_2
Ga	4.0	2,874	C_2H_2
Ge	5.0	2,651	C_2H_2
Hg	1.0	2,537	H_2
In	0.7	3,040	H_2
Li	0.07	6,708	C_2H_2
Mg	0.008	2,852	H_2
Mn	0.03	2,795	H_2
Mo	1.0	3,133	C_2H_2
Ni	0.1	2,320	C_2H_2
Pb	0.5	2,170	C_2H_2
Rb	0.2	7,800	C_2H_2
Sb	1.0	2,175	C_2H_2
Sn	3.0	2,863	C_2H_2
Sr	0.1	4,607	H_2
Te	0.4	2,143	H_2
Zn	0.02	2,139	H_2

[1] From many sources.

Obviously the sensitivity figures listed in Table XI will improve as the atomic absorption method is refined. They have often been exceeded already by optimizing the instrumental parameters. These values are considered to be acceptable under routine working conditions. Various factors such as instrumental settings, fuel-air ratios use of organic solvents, flame height, etc., can be controlled to improve on these values.

SEA WATER

Owing to viscosity, cation and anion interferences, and other effects, the analysis of trace metals in sea water is not as simple and straight-forward as in fresh water. The effects of viscosity on absorption are well known and are illustrated in Fig. 8. Still

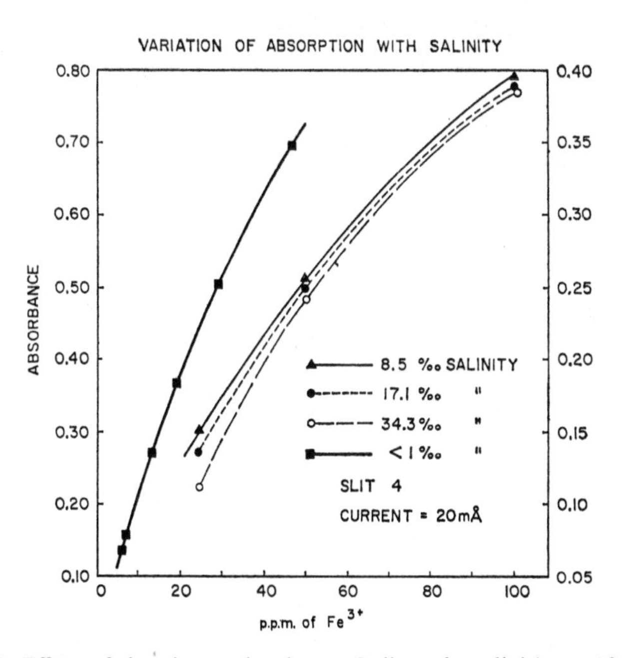

Fig.8. Effects of viscosity on absorbance. Ordinate for salinities < 1 % is on right. Curve obtained on a Perkin–Elmer Model 303 atomic absorption unit with an air-acetylene flame. (E. E. Angino, unpublished data.)

atomic absorption spectrometry has much to recommend it for the quantitative analysis of trace metals in sea water. It is sensitive enough for the analysis of many metals in concentrations in the range of parts per billion to parts per million and it is relatively free from matrix effects. For many elements only minor sample preparation (e.g., filtration) is required.

In one of the earliest applications, if not the first, of atomic absorption spectroscopy to the analysis of sea water, FABRICAND et al. (1962) studied the total concentration of copper, nickel, zinc, iron and manganese in untreated sea water. Metal free containers were used for sample collection and storage. Working curves of the elements studied were made by diluting carefully prepared 0.1% solutions with both distilled and sea water. The latter was used to ascertain the effects of any interferences present. An oxyhydrogen or oxyacetylene flame was used. The unknown was introduced directly into the flame without any prior sample preparation. Results were reported reproducible to within 25%. Better precision for the determinations at the low concentration levels of these elements in sea water is required. Increased precision may be achieved by either preconcentration techniques as described by BURRELL (1965a) or by suitable modification to increase the absorption path.

BILLINGS and HARRISS (1965) determined calcium, magnesium, potassium, sodium, rubidium and strontium in a study of coastal water from the Texas Gulf and British Honduras areas. Samples were aspirated directly into an air-acetylene flame with no sample preparation other than filtration and dilution. No difference in composition was reported between acidified and non-acidified aliquots nor between filtered and unfiltered (W and R Balston 41 filter) samples. These data give total concentration values for sea water. The possibilities of matrix and viscosity effects were overcome by preparing standards from reagent or spectrographic grade chemical to approximate sea water composition plus the desired trace metals. Concentration ranges measured were from 0.1 p.p.m. for Rb to 10,800 p.p.m. for Na. Reproducibility was good. These data provided forceful evidence that specific ionic ratios in sea water are not constant, as has been assumed by many workers. Standard solutions should be made up to appropriate sea water concentrations using any one of several formulas available. That of HARVEY (1960) is used most frequently.

In a subsequent study, initiated on the basis of the results just noted, ANGINO et al. (1966) showed that the Sr content of sea water was indeed quite variable ranging from 5.9–8.0 mg/l. The samples were prepared by filtering through 0.45 μ Millipore membrane filters and then aspirated directly into an air-acetylene flame. Standards were made up containing 10,000 mg/l Na, 1,250 mg/l Mg, 400 mg/lCa, 400 mg/l K and 3.0–12.0 mg/l Sr. Two main sources of error may exist in such standards: (*1*) viscosity difference between standard and samples; and (*2*) affect of anion concentration.

A viscosity difference would effect the aspiration rate. This was tested by measuring the aspirating time of NaCl solutions ranging from 500–12,000 mg/l Na. A decreasing aspiration rate was apparent around 4,000 mg/l sodium; thereafter up to 12,000 mg/l the change was gradual enough that no serious errors resulted, consequently, sample solutions having a viscosity equivalent to that of 4,000–12,000 mg/l Na solutions can be compared to the standards used.

To test for effect of anion concentration, a sample of sea water can be prepared by the method described by HARVEY (1960), to which is added a sufficient amount of the desired metal cation. In the strontium study described 5.0 mg/l Sr were added. Analysis of the sample gave 5.04 mg/l Sr. A test for accuracy of the method was made by analysing five samples by the standard addition method. The average deviation reported between the value for standards and value of additions was 0.2 mg/l Sr and was not systematically high or low. Additional tests should be made to test any errors that might be introduced by reagent contamination, interelemental spectral interferences of molecular absorption. BILLINGS (1965a) has demonstrated that no molecular absorption effects on strontium would be expected in the analysis of sea water by atomic absorption. Although molecular absorption should not be common in trace metal analysis of sea water by atomic absorption, its possible effect should always be expected and a check made to assure its absence.

ANGINO and BILLINGS (1966) reported a method for the direct determination of lithium in sea water without prior chemical separation by use of atomic absorption. The sole preparation involved filtering through a 0.45 μ filter. Subsequent to filtering, the samples were analysed directly with a Perkin–Elmer Model 303 Atomic Absorption Spectrometer using a lithium tube and an air-acetylene flame.

Standards were made up containing 10,000 mg/l Na, 1250 mg/l Mg, 400 mg/l Ca, 400 mg/1 K and 0.05–0.3 mg/l Li. Reagents used were Baker analysed NaCl, MgO and K_2CO_3; Johnson–Matthey Specpure $CaCO_3$ and reagent grade HCl to dissolve the MgO, K_2CO_3 and $CaCO_3$. Chlorides were not used since they might introduce an accuracy problem because of their deliquescence.

Two sources of error may exist in such standards. Since the samples range in salinity there might be a viscosity difference between them and the standards and such a difference could affect the aspiration rate. This effect was tested by the method described above for strontium analysis using these standards. Secondly, to test the effect of anion concentration a sample of artificial sea water was made up by the method described by HARVEY (1960) to which was added 150 μg/l Li. Analysis of this sample by these standards yielded 158 μg/l Li. A second accuracy test was made by analyzing five samples by a standard addition method. The average deviation between the standard values and values by additions was 6 μg/1 Li. Additional tests revealed no errors by molecular absorption reagent contamination or inter-elemental spectral interference. Standard deviation calculated by the usual method was 11 μg/l Li. Lithium concentration ranged from 166 to 218 μg/l and averaged 195 mg/l.

Because of biological cycling and erratic distribution in sea water, iron and manganese are of special interest to oceanographers but their precise measurement has been difficult. Atomic absorption analysis should help alleviate this problem. The metal distribution between the particulate, colloidal and dissolved phases should be studied. JOYNER and FINLEY (1966) examined the use of coprecipitation and extraction techniques in the analysis of iron and manganese from shallow water samples (0–100 m) collected in an area 10–100 miles offshore between the north end of Vancouver Island and the Columbia River mouth. They describe a method for directly extracting these metals from sea water (pH approx. 8.2) by chelation with sodium diethyldithiocarbamate (DEDTC) and extracting into methyl isobutyl ketone.

To 200 ml of sea water contained in 250 ml separatory funnels; known amounts (μg/ml level) of manganese and iron standards and 10 ml of 5% Na-DEDTC were added. After a 15 min. wait, 10.0 ml of MIBK were added, the mixture shaken vigorously for a few minutes and then allowed to stand 20 min. Subsequently, the separated phases were transferred to Babcock bottles. The separatory funnels are then rinsed with deionized water and the washes drained into the Babcock bottles for centrifugation to complete the phase separations. Analyses were made using a stoichiometric air-acetylene flame and appropriate wavelengths. Blank determinations were run similarly. The results shown in Fig. 9 and 10 include all corrections for volume differences. Reproducibility was in the range of 10–20% owing to the low absorbance values recorded.

Several aspects of the technique demand caution in its application to chemical oceanography; among these are: (*1*) low absorbance values limit the precision; (*2*) chelation at the natural pH of sea water ($\sim$ 8.2) gives no guarantee of recovery of any organically bound manganese in true solution.

In a study of the copper content of Irish Sea water MAGEE and RAHMAN (1965) used a combined atomic absorption–extraction method. Place 25 ml of sea water in a 50-ml separatory funnel and add 1 ml of a 1% ammonium pyrrolidine dithiocarbamate solution. Shake the mixture for about 20–30 sec, and add 10 ml of ethyl acetate, shake again for 60 sec. After the phases have separated, drain off the aqueous phase. Filter the acetate phase into a 10 ml volumetric flask and fill to the mark. This solution can be aspirated directly into the flame. Prior to complexing, EDTA should be

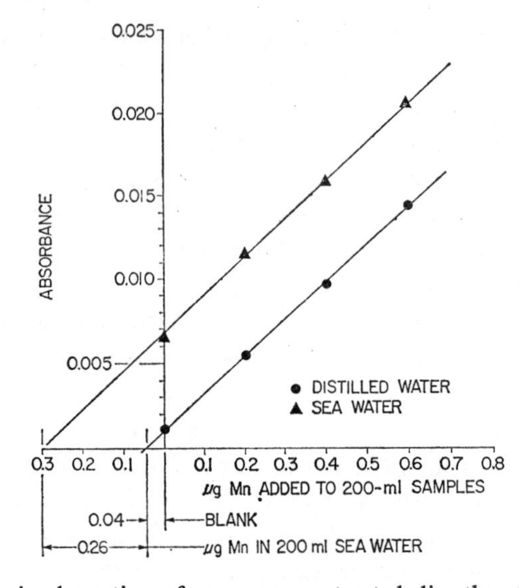

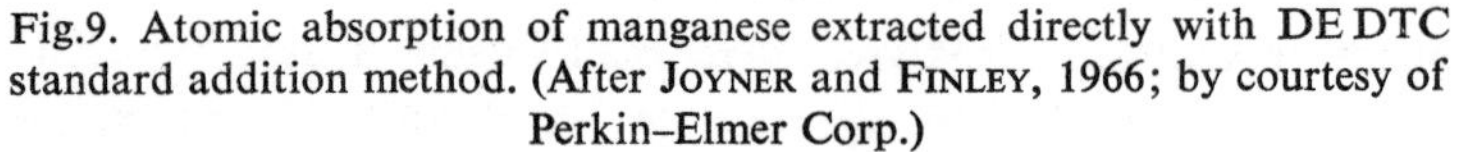

Fig.9. Atomic absorption of manganese extracted directly with DE DTC standard addition method. (After Joyner and Finley, 1966; by courtesy of Perkin–Elmer Corp.)

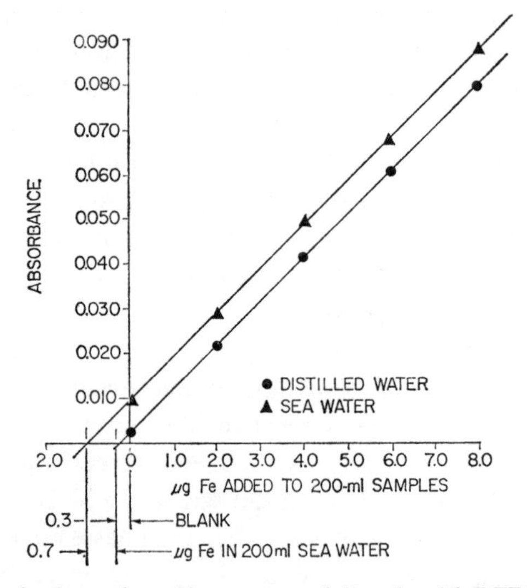

Fig.10. Atomic absorption of iron extracted directly with DEDTC, standard addition method. (After Joyner and Finley, 1966; by courtesy of Perkin–Elmer Corp.)

added as a masking agent. The method has potential for elements in sea water with a chemistry similar to that of copper.

FABRICAND et al. (1966), in a later study reported on the Li, Mg, K, Rb, and Sr content of sea water. All the samples were stored in polyethylene containers and refrigerated until analysed. They employed a Perkin–Elmer long-path burner with an air-acetylene flame. For Li, Sr, and Rb, stock solutions were diluted with artificial sea water to provide appropriate standard solutions. The samples were run directly without dilution. For magnesium, both the stock solutions and samples were diluted by 11,000 with redistilled water. This is done to reduce the magnesium concentration to the 1 p.p.m. range. For K, artificial sea water containing no K was mixed with the stock solution in appropriate amounts to yield a solution with a salinity approximately that of sea water. This solution and the samples were then diluted by 1/100 with redistilled water and the K content measured.

No observable effect was noted on the Mg and Sr absorptions that could have been caused by other major constituents of sea water. The use of artificial sea water negated the effect of Na on the absorptions of the alkali metals. Inasmuch as the samples were not filtered these results are "total values" for each sample. Results were as follows on 21 samples taken at depths of 16–4,800 m at 10°59′N 49°36′W Li 169 ± 3 μg/kg, Mg 1279 ± 23 mg/kg, K 384 ± 7 mg/kg, Rb 102 ± 9 μg/kg, and Sr 7.90 ± 0.16 mg/kg.

BRINES

One of the more difficult types of water to analyse for trace constituents has been brines, both industrial liquids and oil field brines. Most of the analytical techniques prescribed for their analysis are time consuming, laborious, and subject to considerable error. The simple determination of trace metals in sea water by atomic absorption suggested that similar procedures could be used for brines.

SPRAGUE and SLAVIN (1964a) describe a method for quantitatively extracting copper, lead, cadmium, iron, manganese, cobalt,and nickel from concentrated KCl brines. Ammonium pyrrolidine dithiocarbamate (APDC) was used as a chelating agent. A particular advantage of APDC is that it is not specific but will chelate a large number of metals; excepting the alkalis and alkaline earths, over broad pH ranges. The APDC is then taken up in methyl isobutyl ketone (MIBK) and run directly into an air-acetylene flame. This procedure allows the trace metals to be concentrated easily 10–100 times in the organic solvent and further increases the sensitivity of the method by the known enhancement of the organic solvent. A KCl (sylvite) sample from Carlsbad, New Mexico was dissolved in distilled water. A 25% KCl solution and appropriate metal standards were prepared. Adjust the sample and standards to pH 2.8 by adding HCl drop by drop. Place 25 ml aliquots of the sample, standards, and water blank in 60 ml separatory funnels and add 1 ml of a 5% aqueous solution of APDC and 5 ml of MIBK to each funnel. Shake for a few minutes and drain off the aqueous layer and aspirate the remaining ketone solution into the flame. Results compare favorably with colorimetric determination and are obtained more simply and more rapidly.

DELAUGHTER (1965) describes a method of extracting copper, iron, manganese, and nickel at the parts per billion level from NaCl brines by extraction with MIBK, using cupferron as a chelating agent. All four metals are extracted simultaneously at a pH of 7. Molybdenum is extracted into MIBK after chelation with 4-methyl-1, 2-dimercaptobenzene (dithiol), chromium is extracted into the same solvent by means of diphenyl-thiocarbazone (DPTC). The method should be applicable to both oil field brines and sea water.

The desired reagents can be prepared by placing 0.1 g of DPTC in a 100 ml volumetric flask and filling to the mark with MIBK. A solution of dithiol in 1% NaOH is prepared by dissolving 1 g of dithiol in 500 ml of 1% NaOH. The solution is mixed well and thioglycolic acid (concentrated reagent grade) added dropwise and mixed after each drop. When a faint but permanent opalescence appears the end point has been reached. Store the solutions in a cool place. Do not allow dithiol to contact the skin!

The chromium must remain in the hexavalent state for the reaction and chelation. The method of additions is used after preparing appropriate standards. Using an air-acetylene flame, no interferences have been reported from other trace metals found in the brines. All the metals can be easily detected to 1 p.p.b. with an 800 g brine sample.

Extraction techniques of trace metals from NaCl brines are also described by MANSELL and EMMELL (1965). APDC was found to quantitatively extract cobalt, chromium molybdenum, nickel and vanadium into MIBK from a 25% NaCl solution at pH 4. Similarly oxine extracts cobalt, copper, molybdenum and nickel into chloroform at pH 9.

The APDC extractions of 25% NaCl solutions were accomplished at pH 4 and 5 ml of 2% APDC solution was added to 50 ml volume of the 25% NaCl solution. Solutions were heated to incipient boiling and cooled. Extraction into 20 ml MIBK was accomplished by manual shaking for one minute.

For the oxine extraction, 50 g of a 50% NaOH solution is partially neutralized with 45 ml of HCl. Five ml of 10% ammonium tartrate are added and the pH adjusted to 9.0 by additional HCl. Dilute the solution to 175 ml, transfer to a 250 ml separatory funnel and add 10 ml of a 1.0% oxine solution in chloroform. Shake for a few minutes and drain the chloroform into a beaker, repeat extraction with 10 ml of chloroform and combine the extracts. Evaporate the chloroform and add 10 ml of water to the beaker and evaporate to eliminate residual oxine. Dissolve the residue in 2 ml of HCl and dilute with methanol to the mark in a 25 ml volumetric flask. Standard solutions are prepared by evaporation of aqueous solutions of the desired metals and treated similarly with HCl and methanol. The methanol solutions are aspirated directly into an air acetylene flame.

Extraction efficiencies for APDC and oxine are given in Tables XII and XIII. A combination of atomic absorption, chemical and emission spectrographic procedures were used to determine re-

TABLE XII

APDC EXTRACTION EFFICIENCY[1]

Element	*μg/ml added*	*μg/ml recovered*	*% recovered*
	1	0.97	97
Chromium	3	3.01	100.3
	5	4.50	90
	1	1.00	100
Vanadium	3	2.91	97
	5	4.55	91
	1	0.98	98
Molybdenum	3	2.97	99
	5	4.57	91
	5	5.0	100
Manganese	10	9.3	93
	25	23.5	94

[1] After MANSELL and EMMEL (1965); reproduced by courtesy of Perkin-Elmer Corp.

TABLE XIII

EXTRACTION EFFICIENCY FOR OXINE FROM WATER AND NACL SOLUTIONS[1]

Element	*μg/ml added*	*Extraction from water (μg/ml found)*	*Extraction from NaCl (μg/ml found)*	*% recovery on NaCl*
Copper	0.05	0.045	0.05	100
	0.100	0.094	0.100	100
	0.200	0.190	0.200	100
	0.400	0.382	0.370	93
Manganese	0.05	0.05	0.05	100
	0.100	0.098	0.100	100
	0.200	0.196	0.200	100
	0.400	0.374	0.384	96
Cobalt	0.05	0.046	0.05	100
	0.100	0.094	0.100	100
	0.200	0.186	0.200	100
	0.400	0.372	0.392	98
Nickel	0.055	0.050	0.055	100
	0.110	0.102	0.110	100
	0.220	0.208	0.220	100
	0.440	0.416	0.440	100

[1] After MANSELL and EMMELL (1965); reproduced by courtesy of Perkin-Elmer Corp.

coveries. The extraction procedures using APDC and oxine as chelating agents for separation of selected trace metals from brine are quantitative and reliable and have much to recommend them. The application of such extraction procedures to the study of the trace metal content of oil field brines will expand.

BILLINGS (1965a) has described a method for the determination of potassium in oil field brines using an Osram discharge lamp. If the brine has a precipitate, HCl is added to cause resolution. After filtering the brine (0.45 μ), it is diluted sufficiently to place the potassium concentration into the linear portion of the working curves. The dilution factor will, of course, vary from sample to sample, depending on the sample concentrations. Both the standard curve and the standard addition method was used. Care is required as the known high Na content of oil field brines can cause enhancement of the K absorption signal. The standard addition method gives the most reliable data. The brines were aspirated directly into an air-propane flame. A coefficient of variation of $\pm$ 0.8% is reported. No interferences other than ionization interference by Na was noted. Potassium content of the brines studied ranged from 120–1,280 mg/l.

A similar method and approach for strontium in brines is given by BILLINGS and ANGINO (1965). The coefficient of variation was $\pm$ 2% calculated from twelve aliquots from one brine. A comparison of results using the standard curve and standard addition methods indicated no appreciable difference between the two methods. No interferences from viscosity, molecular absorption or matrix effects were reported. The determination of strontium and potassium in oil field brines by atomic absorption spectrometry appears to be simple, rapid, and precise and the extension of the techniques described here to a study of other trace elements in brines seems warranted.

CHAPTER 6

Ore analysis

INTRODUCTION

In atomic absorption spectroscopy geologists and geochemists have a rapid and simple means of determining the concentrations of many metals in ores. To date reported interferences are few. The application of atomic absorption to the study of the metallic content of ores is only limited by the requirement that the sample must be in solution. This is seldom a problem as simple and rapid procedures are available. Once the ores are in solution, few problems remain.

Analyses have been reported for many metals, commonly in concentrations below 0.1 p.p.m. in solutions. Detection limits are even lower. Standard atomic absorption techniques are rapidly replacing classical gravimetric and volumetric methods. Since the method itself is so simple, most of the discussion here will center on sample preparation. Because of variations in ore types, a sample matrix may dictate appropriate modifications of any of the procedures mentioned. For the purpose of compactness of subject matter we have included the discussion of the analyses of petroleum crude oils in this chapter.

COPPER, ZINC, LEAD, NICKEL

In one of the earliest applications of atomic absorption to ore studies, STRASHEIM et al. (1960) determined Cu in ores, concentrates and tailings. Their equipment consisted of a Hilger and Watts Uvispek spectrometer with atomic absorption attachments.

In their investigation, samples of 0.5 g Cu ore were dissolved in various acid mixtures to determine the best acid combinations. Of those tested, the most successful acid mixtures to dissolve a 0.5 g sample were, in order:

(*1*) 10 ml 40% HF, 10 ml concentrated HNO_3.
(*2*) 10 ml concentrated H_2SO_4, 10 ml concentrated HNO_3.
(*3*) 10 ml concentrated HCl, 10 ml concentrated HNO_3.

The samples were leached and heated for 40 min. in a mixture of the first-named set. Each solution was filtered, the first 30 ml discarded, and the next 30 ml transferred to a 200 ml volumetric flask and made up to the volume. The analysis was made using the 3,247 Å Cu line, and comparing the results with artificial standard solutions. Since the most effective acid mixtures for an ore sample from any given area will be determined by the type of rock and minerals containing the Cu, the best mixture for specific samples will have to be determined by each analyst.

The presence of calcium, sodium, iron, chromium and cobalt up to 1% in the solution and acid concentrations of 1*N* H_2SO_4 and HCl did not interfere with the copper determination. For copper in solution, in the range 2–100 p.p.m., the coefficient of variation did not exceed 3%. In a comparison of results the atomic absorption ore analyses generally agreed with chemical values within 5% of the amount present.

In another method described by FARRAR (1965), 100 mg samples of copper and zinc ore are weighed and transferred to 300 ml Erlenmeyer flasks, 12.5 g of $NaHSO_4$ added, and the mixture heated for 30 min. The contents are transferred to appropriate containers, fused and cooled. One hundred ml of H_2O and 15 ml of HCl are added, heat is reapplied to attain solution, and the contents are then recooled and filtered into a 1-l volumetric flask. Determinations by atomic absorption are made against aqueous copper nitrate standards containing sulfate concentrations similar to that of the samples. In a test of analytical precision two ore samples were tested for copper and zinc on different days. The coefficient of variation was less than 1.5% and agreement with wet chemical values was within 3% of the amount present in each instance.

Farrar devised another preparative scheme that is described in SLAVIN (1965). The ore sample is ground to 150 μ. A 0.5 g sample is then extracted with an HCl–HNO_3 mixture, 10 ml of 1:1 H_2SO_4 added and the resulting solution fumed. Subsequently, it is diluted to 1 l with H_2O and copper determined directly. Zinc is measured in a 1:10 dilution of this solution. Nickel can also be determined by this technique. For nickel, a 1-g sample is prepared similarly but diluted to 200 ml. Lead can also be determined by this procedure. Standard solutions are used throughout. No interference from any metals in the ore samples has been reported.

For copper concentrates (FARRAR, 1965), the preparative step is slightly more involved. A 0.25 g sample (finely ground) is weighed into a 400 ml beaker, dispersed with 10 ml of water and 2 ml of bromine; and allowed to stand for 10 min. with the beaker covered. Ten ml of HNO_3 are added and heat is applied slowly to drive off the bromine. Five ml of $HClO_4$ and 6 drops of HF are added and the solution is heated until fume evolution occurs. The beaker is covered, refluxed for 20 min. and cooled. Subsequently, 100 ml water, 1 g of tartaric acid and 25 ml of a saturated ammonium acetate solution are added. After boiling for 10 min., cooling and filtering into a 250 ml volumetric flask and washing again with hot water, the solution is recooled, diluted to volume and mixed. Lead, copper and zinc are determined from this solution, with dilution where necessary. Agreement with more laborious wet chemical methods is good.

MEDDING (1966) uses atomic absorption in routine assays for iron, nickel, copper and cobalt. Incoming ore is usually within the range of 40% iron, 10% nickel, 3% copper and 0.3% cobalt.

A 0.25 g sample of ore is dissolved with an H_2SO_4–HNO_3 mixture to which persulfate is added as an oxidizer. After evaporating to dryness, the solids are redissolved in dilute H_2SO_4 and diluted to 100 ml. Cobalt is determined directly on this solution. Following a further 1:10 dilution the concentration of copper, nickel and iron is measured. The coefficient of variation for the full procedure is nickel 0.8, cobalt 1.3, copper 0.6 and iron 2.5%, respectively.

ZINC AND CADMIUM

The determination of zinc and cadmium in ores by atomic absorption is reported by FIXMAN and BOUGHTON (1966). Samples for zinc and cadmium analyses are treated in the following manner:

Each sample (0.2 g) is digested in a solution of 15 ml concentrated HCl, 10 ml of concentrated HNO_3 and 10 ml of mineral-free water and evaporated to dryness. The sample is then taken back into solution in boiling 5% HCl and diluted to 100 ml. Cadmium can be run directly on this solution. Owing to the extreme sensitivity of atomic absorption, greater dilution is necessary for zinc determinations. Appropriate zinc and cadmium lines are used in an acetylene-air flame with a Walsh burner. A comparison of atomic

TABLE XIV

ZINC AND CADMIUM IN ORES AND CONCENTRATE[1]

	Zn%		*Cd%*	
Sample	*A.A.*[2]	*Wet*	*A.A.*	*Wet*
1	62.17	61.80	0.366	0.400
2	52.87	52.80	0.240	0.255
3	47.54	47.40	0.219	0.218
4	31.25	30.79	0.128	0.123
5	58.10	57.30	0.279	0.255
6	57.81	57.30	0.257	0.275
7	0.56	0.7		
8	1.25	1.1		
9	3.50	3.7		
10	14.9	14.4		
11	10.4	9.9		
12	5.73	6.05	0.050	0.053
13	1.50	1.8		

[1] Samples *1–6* are zinc concentrates, *7–13* are ore samples. Atomic absorption has replaced conventional means in these analyses of Cd and Zn in ore samples. Improved precision is also achieved. (After FIXMAN, 1966.)

[2] A.A. = atomic absorption.

absorption results with wet chemical analysis of the samples analysed for zinc and cadmium is given in Table XIV.

In a later study FARRAR (1966) described a similar but modified technique for the determination of cadmium in ores. One gram of ore is placed in 250 ml beaker and 10 ml each of H_2O and HNO_3. The sample is digested by heating for 15 min. (To high sulfide ores add 1 ml bromine.) Add approximately 10 ml of HCl and digest 10 min., add 10 ml of $HClO_4$ and fume. Cover the beaker and boil the solution for 15 min. Cool and rinse the cover and beaker sides with hot water until about 175 ml of solution is obtained. Simmer for 5 min., cool and filter into a 250 ml volumetric flask, wash beaker with cold water and transfer to the flask. Fill flask to mark and mix. This solution can be aspirated directly into the flame. Table XV compares results obtained by atomic absorption and by

TABLE XV

PERCENT CADMIUM IN ORES[1]

Atomic absorption	*Gravimetric*
0.18	0.18
0.57	0.55
0.33	0.35
0.16	0.165
0.23	0.225
0.14	0.143

[1] Modified after FARRAR (1966).

gravimetric methods. Good reproducibility for the method is reported.

MERCURY

In the technique described by VAUGHN and McCARTHY (1964) of the U.S. Geological Survey, a one gram sample is heated in an appropriate holder to 500°C by 400-kc radio frequency energy. The mercury is vaporized and trapped by amalgamation with gold. The chief interferents, smoke and gasses, are allowed to pass off:

subsequently mercury trapped on the gold is volatized by heating the gold and the mercury vapor passed into an absorption chamber. An analog signal, produced when the mercury vapor absorbs (at 2,537 Å) ultraviolet light, is converted to digital form and calibrated to mercury concentration. Spectrographic and atomic absorption analysis of jasperoid and siliceous limestone samples show good agreement. The lower limit of sensitivity using a 1-g sample is 5 p.p.b. The method has been tested successfully in the field. The use of this method in geochemical prospecting for mercury is described by VAUGHN (1967).

SILVER

RAWLING et al. (1961) described an atomic absorption method used to replace the standard fire assay technique for silver in lead–sulfide concentrates. The silver content in the lead–sulfide concentrate is about 20 ounce/ton (1 ounce/ton equals about 35 p.p.m.). Four grams of ground concentrate are dissolved with 100 ml of 10N HCl and warmed. When solution is completed, 5 ml of 16N HNO_3 are added and the solution boiled until the volume is reduced 50%. The solution and precipitated lead chloride are transferred to a 100 ml volumetric flask and taken up to volume with 50% v/v HCl. This solution will hold 25 p.p.m. silver. Atomic absorption measurements were made using the 3,280 Å line of silver. Tests showed no interference on the atomic absorption of a 10 p.p.m. silver solution of 100 p.p.m. Mn^{2+}, Co^{2+}, Cd^{2+}, Mg^{2+}, Ca^{2+}, As^{5+}, Sb, F^-, PO_4^{3-}, and SiO_3^{2-}, and of 0.01% 0.05%, 0.1% and 0.2% of Cu^{2+}, Fe^{3+}, Zn^{2+} and Pb^{2+}, respectively. An air-coal gas flame was used. A 1.3% coefficient of variation was obtained on several samples at the 15–20 ounce/ton level. Although the precision obtained is equal to that of the fire assay method, the results averaged 0.5 ounce/ton higher.

The simplicity of operation, compactness and reasonable equipment price are such that the method may be expected to supercede the fire assay method for silver determination in many types of ore material. The analytical sensitivity is adequate and ore samples in the range 4–15 ounce/ton present no problem. No interferences have been reported.

The acid solution requirement can be avoided (GREAVES, 1963) by complexing the lead and silver salts with the addition of diethylene triamine. This keeps the ions in solution over a wide pH range.

FIXMAN and BOUGHTON (1966) describe a different approach for routine silver assay. The samples are prepared as follows: put a 0.2 g sample into solution by digestion with 25 ml of concentrated HNO_3, 2 ml of 15% H_2O_2 and 10 ml of demineralized water. Evaporate the solutions until just moist, then redissolve in boiling 5% HNO_3 and dilute to 50 ml with water. Dilutions are made of each sample so that solution concentrations of less than 3 p.p.m. silver are used for absorption measurement. An air-acetylene flame is used. Results agree well with fire assay analyses (Table XVI).

A somewhat different approach is used by TINDALL (1965). To 10 g samples in 400 ml beakers, add 25 ml of concentrated HCl. Cover the beakers, heat for 20 min., then add 15 ml of concentrated HNO_3 and allow the contents to digest (covered) for 30 min. Subsequently, the covers are removed, the contents taken to dryness and baked until no odor of HNO_3 remains. When cool, dissolve the salts with 25 ml each of concentrated HCl and H_2O_2, then recool to about 20°C and dilute to 100 ml in Nessler color tubes. The solutions are then filtered into 125 ml Erlenmeyer flasks and capped until used. Silver is determined at 3,280 Å in an oxidizing flame using an air-acetylene gas mixture.

TABLE XVI

SILVER ASSAY (OUNCE/TON) CONCENTRATES AT HIGHER LEVELS[1]

A.A.[2]	*Fire*	*A.A.*	*Fire*
0.09	0.15	11.4	11.3
1.25	1.50	27.7	28.6
1.92	1.60	120	118
3.73	3.70	152	149
4.79	5.10	181	182

[1] Modified after SLAVIN (1965); reproduced by courtesy of Perkin–Elmer Corp.

[2] A.A. = atomic absorption.

Samples with a high lead content are troublesome, since lead chloride tends to crystallize, trapping some of the silver. For such ores, the addition of ammonium acetate or ammonium chloride will keep the salt in solution. With such samples the accuracy of silver determination can be impoved by using a smaller sample size. Some modification to this method is given in TINDALL (1966).

An acid dissolution technique for the analysis of Ag in mineralized rock has been presented by HUFFMAN et al. (1966). The procedure is straightforward. Moisten a 1 g sample of rock powder in a 100 ml beaker with 2 ml of water, then add 10 ml of concentrated HNO_3 and cover the beaker with a watchglass. Subsequent to reaction, place the covered beaker on a hot plate and boil the solution gently for about 15 min. Swirl the beaker occasionally to assure mixing of the solution. Cool, add 25 ml of water and heat on a steam bath for 30 min. Transfer the solution and any insoluble material to a 50 ml volumetric flask, cool dilute to volume and mix. Decant half of the 50 ml solution and centrifuge for 5 min .Measure the absorbance of the clear solution by aspirating directly into an air-acetylene flame.

Comparative studies were made using two different acid decomposition procedures (reflux boiling with HNO_3 and complete decomposition with HNO_3, HF, and $HClO_3$) and comparison with fire assay data show that the accuracy is good regardless of the method used. Tests for interferences from other ions or elements in solution were done by analyzing different ore minerals (Table XVII). No interference in the determination of silver in these samples was noted. No special treatment was made on any sample prior to aspirating the solution into the flame.

GOLD

Neither X-ray fluorescence nor emission spectrography are practical for determining gold at the 0.001 to 1 troy ounce/ton level; OLSEN (1965) examined the usefulness of several atomic absorption techniques as a gold assay method for siliceous carbonate

TABLE XVII

COMPARISON OF ATOMIC-ABSORPTION DETERMINATION OF SILVER WITH THE GEOCHEMICAL COLORIMETRIC METHOD ON IMPURE MINERALS OF DIVERSE COMPOSITION[1]

Nominal mineral	*Principal elements of potential analytical interference*	*Silver (p.p.m.)*		
		Atomic absorption		
		Complete solution with acids	*Nitric acid boil*	*Geochemical colorimetric field test*[2]
Cervantite	Sb	1	1	0.5
Psilomelane	Mn	1	1	0.5
Descloizite	Pb, Zn, V, Cu	1	1	0.7
Allanite	Rare-earth elements.	5	3	2
Pyrite	Fe	7	6	4
Pentlandite	Ni	3	3	4
Pyrrhotite	Fe, Cu, Ni	5	4	3.5
Hemimorphite	Zn, Si (sol.), Cd	4	4	3.5
Arsenical gold ore.	As	5	5	7.5
Glauconite	K, Fe, Si (sol.)	10	8	10
Molybdenite	Mo, Ti	24	16	10
Hydrozincite	Zn	14	14	30
Arsenopyrite	As, Fe	16	16	30
Thorite	Th, P, rare-earth elements.	8	9	>8
Niccolite	Ni, As	34	32	50
Chalcopyrite	Cu, Fe, Bi	158	155	150
Cerussite	Pb	180	175	100
Native antimony.	Sb		170	200
Galena	Pb	600	600	600
Scheelite	W, Pb	315	430	400
Anglesite	Pb	1,090	970	500
Smaltite	As, Co	1,550	1,530	>1,600
Tetrahedrite	Sb, Cu, Mn, Fe	8,200	8,000	4,000

[1] From HUFFMAN et al. (1966).
[2] See NAKAGAWA and LAKIN (1965).

(limestone) ores. The minimum gold content was as low as 0.001 troy ounce/ton.

Of the four techniques tried—(*1*) direct analysis of acid solutions,

(*2*) organic solvent extraction, (*3*) fusion, and (*4*) cyanide extraction, the latter method was preferred.

It is informative to determine why the other methods were not satisfactory, as similar problems might arise in preparing samples of other ore types for analysis. In the acid solution method, the sample is dissolved in aqua regia or combinations of aqua regia and other acids. The method failed for two reasons: (*1*) HF was required for complete sample decomposition, however the HF reacted with the sample and formed a hydroxyfluoride that absorbed the gold; and (*2*) the high calcium concentration in the solution caused so much molecular absorption in the flame that the background reading exceeded by several times the desired signal.

For the organic solvent extraction, the sample is dissolved in various acids and acid combinations. The gold is then extracted in an organic solvent (e.g., isopropyl ether), separated, and the solvent layer analysed. As in the acid method, HF was required to decompose the sample and the hydroxy-fluoride formed, causing emulsification during extraction. While the emulsion problem can be overcome, and the method made to work, its complexity makes it a marginal technique for plant use.

The fusion method uses the first step of fire assaying to decompose the sample. The gold from the sample is contained in a lead "pill". Subsequently, the "pill" is dissolved in aqua regia and the gold content measured by atomic absorption. While useable, the time involved, the necessity of extra equipment, and the need for using a fire-assay furnace for the first step makes the fusion method a marginal one in competition with the normal fire assay technique.

The cyanide method mentioned by OLSEN (1965) is described in considerable detail by SIMMONS (1965). For the cyanide method, 30 g of sample (sized to 150 μ) are weighed in an evaporating dish and ignited for 1 h at 450–600°C. The temperature is kept below 650°C to prevent any clay present from sintering and thereby trapping gold and reducing the accuracy of the analysis. Subsequent to cooling, transfer the sample to a 60 ml shaking jar and add about 0.5 g of CaO and exactly 30 ml of 0.25% NaCN at a temperature of 0.0–95°C. Shake the jar mechanically for 15 min. under proper heat to maintain sample temperature. Treat the contents with a flocculating agent (e.g., 2–4 drops of a 0.5% solution of Separan NP-10), shake gently and vacuum filter (not greater than 15 inches of Hg) through No.1 or No.2 Whatman paper. The solution is then analysed in an air-acetylene flame.

Some 68 samples ranging from soft sandy ore, high in gold content, to tailings (0.05–2 ounces/ton) were analysed and compared with three independent fire assays. The results by atomic absorption agreed with the average of the fire assay better than the three independent assays agreed with each other, demonstrating the equivalent accuracy of the two methods (Table XVIII). Gold ore samples can be assayed by atomic absorption with a 1% accuracy at a gold concentration of 0.5 troy ounces/ton. The agreement between atomic absorption and fire assay methods over the range 0.05–1 ounce/ton was about 2%. Interferences were not encountered. High concentrations of pyrite, carbon and sulfur in samples must be removed prior to analyses as they cause precipitation of gold during processing. Barite in high enough concentration prevents dissolution of the gold even after ignition. The action of barite to inhibit dissolution suggests the possible use of atomic absorption to test which ores may be refractory to cyanide treatment.

To avoid the use of cyanide, TINDALL (1965) developed a method using solvent extraction. Seventy-five ml of each of the samples, prepared as previously described for Tindall's silver method, are placed in 125 ml separatory funnels, Add 2 ml of 48% HBr and

TABLE XVIII

GOLD ASSAY (OUNCE/TON)[1]

No. of samples	*Range–Au ounce/ton ore*		*Fire assays*			*Average*	*Atomic absorption*
			A	*B*	*C*		
13	0.05	0.10	0.072	0.086	0.086	0.081	0.085
67	0.05	2.0	0.314	0.323	0.318	0.318	0.324
43	0.09	0.52	0.229	0.238	0.242	0.236	0.237
11	0.6	2.0	0.93	0.94	0.89	0.92	0.95

[1] After SLAVIN (1965); reproduced by courtesy of Perkin–Elmer Corp.

15 ml of methyl isobutyl ketone (MIBK) (also designated correctly 2-methyl-4 pentanone). Shake the funnels vigorously for 15 sec. and allow them to stand until the layers separate then drain and discard most of the aqueous layer. As MIBK is toxic, it should be used either in a fume hood or a well ventilated area.

Add 10 to 15 ml of a wash solution (10 ml HBr and 10 ml HCl diluted to 500 ml total volume) to each funnel and shake for 10 sec. The aqueous portion is drained and the process repeated until the MIBK, solution is clear. Yellow colorations owing to iron do not interfere. After draining all of the aqueous portion and some of the MIBK the remaining MIBK solution is collected in a 25 ml Erlenmeyer flask and the flask stoppered. Using this technique, the burner used (10 cm slotted Walsh type) required frequent cleaning; the amount of cleaning being dependent on the time that MIBK is burned rather than on the number of samples run.

A comparison of average results for assayed heads and calculated heads indicated that atomic absorption provided a sensitivity comparable to that of the fire assay method and a somewhat superior precision. No serious interferences are reported. The use of a cyanide–atomic absorption method in the study and geochemical prospecting of gold-bearing sedimentary rocks is described by ANTWEILER and LOVE (1967).

DETERMINATION OF TRACE METALS IN PETROLEUM CRUDE OIL

Atomic absorption has proven to be an effective means of analysing the metal content of petroleum crudes. The method is rapid, relatively free from matrix interferences and sensitive to non-aqueous samples. While X-ray fluorescence and emission spectroscopy can both detect metals at the desired low concentrations, neither of these techniques are easily used for liquids. The determination of copper, nickel, and iron in crude petroleums by atomic absorption is now common practice in many laboratories. The major concern is, as usual, that of finding the best means of preparing the crudes for aspiration. In one method (BARRAS, 1962)

TABLE XIX

TRACE ELEMENT DATA FOR PETROLEUM CRUDE OIL (CONCENTRATION IN P.P.M.)[1]

Analysis	*Sample No. 1*			*Sample No. 2*			*Sample No. 3*		
	Ni	*Fe*	*Cu*	*Ni*	*Fe*	*Cu*	*Ni*	*Fe*	*Cu*
1	0.70	0.90	0.12	1.60	1.55	0.26	1.70	1.80	0.29
2	0.75	0.80	0.12	1.60	1.50	0.25	1.80	1.70	0.26
3	0.80	0.80	0.12	1.60	1.50	0.23	1.70	1.80	0.29
4	0.80	0.80	0.12	1.65	1.50	0.23	1.80	1.75	0.26
5	0.75	0.75	0.11	1.60	1.55	0.25	1.80	1.75	0.26
6	0.75	0.75	0.15	1.65	1.50	0.21	1.75	1.70	0.25
Average	0.75	0.80	0.12	1.62	1.52	0.24	1.76	1.75	0.27

[1] After BARRAS (1962); reproduced by courtesy of Jarrell–Ash Co.

oil is diluted in the ratio of 1:3 v/v with *n*-heptane and aspirated directly into an oxy-hydrogen flame using a three burner system. Other solvents such as xylene, *n*-pentane, *n*-hexane and iso-octane would also have served. Toluene and benzene are not recommended as they cause a decrease in flame sensitivity for many metals. The metals are determined easily at concentrations as low as 0.1 p.p.m. using the multi-pass system. Reproducibility data for copper, nickel, and iron for six runs on three samples are shown in Table XIX. At concentration levels of 0.1 p.p.m., a 10% coefficient of variation is apparently possible. Recovery experiments verified this method to about 0.05 p.p.m. for these three metals. For the diluted oils, a standard deviation of about 0.02 p.p.m. was obtained. The 2,320 Å, 2,483 Å, and 3,247 Å lines were used for the nickel, iron and copper analyses, respectively.

Still another method of sample preparation is to dilute the oils 1:3 by volume with a mixture containing $13^1/_3$% *p*-xylene, 20% 2-ethylhexanoic acid and $66^2/_3$% *n*-heptane. Heat the samples to 85°C and allow them to cool to room temperature. Subsequent to cooling, the samples can be aspirated directly into the flame.

An important consideration in working with crude petroleums is to assure that the viscosity of samples and standards are matched. The viscosity differences can cause differences in aspirating rates by a factor of 3–4 times. Such variations will cause errors in the concentration value readings of trace metals in crude oils and must be corrected. If using the above described methods, this can be accomplished satisfactorily by diluting the standards 1:3 by volume with *n*-heptane. Owing to the viscosity problem, the preparation of standards for petroleum crudes is not quite as simple a procedure as for other samples. Therefore, it is appropriate to present one method of standard preparation that proved of value in the previously described studies. Dissolve an appropriate amount of dried Ni, Cu, or Fe cyclohexane butyrate (to make a 500 p.p.m. metal solution) in a warm mixture containing 2 ml xylene, 4 ml of 2-ethylhexanoic acid. To this solution is added sufficient medicinal white oil to make 100 g. Dilute as required. Organo-metallic standards, some of which are metal cyclohexane butyrates, for use in studies of crude oil trace metal content are available from the National Bureau of Standards. These methods have proven acceptable using a Jarrell–Ash atomic absorption unit with a 3 burner system and an air-hydrogen fuel mixture.

Many other metals such as Ag, Cr, Ba, Na, Pb, Fe, and Mg have been determined in lubricating oils and catalytic cracking feedstocks. Many of the techniques used there would be applicable to the analyses of these metals in crudes. SPRAGUE and SLAVIN (1963), TRENT and SLAVIN (1964a), MEANS and RATCLIFF (1965), and BURROWS et al. (1965), have described such methods. Interelement effects are negligible. Limiting sensitivities ranged from 0.01 p.p.m. for Cu to 2.0 p.p.m. for Ba.

CAPACHO-DELGADO and MANNING (1966) describe an atomic absorption technique for the determination of vanadium in gas oils. The data were obtained with a Perkin–Elmer 303 Atomic Absorption Spectrophotometer using the 3,184 Å vanadium line, a high intensity hollow cathode tube, and a nitrous oxide-acetylene flame. The detection limit was 0.05 μg/ml vanadium. The method of addition was used. A 500 μg/ml vanadium standard was made from bis (1-phenyl-1, 3-butanediono) oxo-vanadium (IV). The standard is diluted 10 × with xylene to give a 50 μg/ml vanadium standard in 90% xylene. Add Aliquots of the 50 mg/ml standard to equal portions of gas-oil sample and dilute with xylene. For example, 8.3 ml of gas oil can be put into a 25 ml volumetric flask and 1 ml of the 50 mg/ml vanadium standard solution added. The contents are mixed and then diluted to the mark with xylene. This will give a 3 × dilution of the gas oil, with 2 μg/ml vanadium in addition to the unknown amount present in the sample. Dilution of the gas-oil with xylene is reported to improve the efficiency of nebulization. Dilutions can be prepared with the desired amounts of vanadium. Results compared well with emission spectrographic data. Repeated determinations showed good precision.

When analysing viscous materials such as crude petroleums, the sensitivity is very definitely related to aspiration rate. Since the aspiration rates of dilute oils will vary, the method of standard additions is recommended in the study of petroleum crudes. It is, of course, independent of viscosity effects.

TRENT and SLAVIN (1964a) compared the absorption of oils of different dilutions. They concluded that there was no advantage to using more concentrated oils. Even though they aspirated and burned satisfactorily, greater scattering was obtained with the more concentrated oils. KERBER (1966) used a modified standard additions method that yielded a precision of 0.05 p.p.m. Ni. His study showed that under certain conditions a 1:5 dilution of the sample with *p*-xylene gives better results than the 1:3 dilution used by BARRAS (1962).

COAL ASH

Many of the classical methods of coal ash analysis are involved and laborious. These difficulties are avoided by use of atomic absorption spectrometry.

BELCHER and BROOKS (1963) present a method for determination of Sr in coal ash which is also adaptable to Mg and Ca. The procedure provides for a concentration range of 0.01–2% Sr in the coal. Place a weighted sample of about 100 mg of ground coal ash into a 30 ml platinum crucible. Add 5 ml of HF (s.g. 1.13) and heat to effect solution; add 4 ml of perchloric acid (s.g. 1.70) and fume for 2 min. Cool and wash with a few drops of HCl (s.g. 1.16) and fume until salts begin te separate. Cool and then add 20 ml 5% v/v HF and warm to obtain complete dissolution. Transfer to a 100 ml volumetric flask and add 4.0 ml of a 5% lanthanum solution in 25% v/v HCl. Dilute to mark with distilled water. This solution is aspirated directly into an air-acetylene flame. Standard solutions should be prepared with 0.2% lanthanum in 1% v/v HCl covering the desired range. The strontium content in the ash can be back calculated from the measured concentration data.

A similar method can be used for Mg and Ca. Both the Mg and Ca standard solutions should contain 0.2% lanthanum in 1% v/v HCl. Calcium standards should contain in addition 1.5% v/v perchloric acid. The method provides for 0.01–2% calcium and 0.001–0.2% magnesium in the ash.

OBERMILLER and FREEDMAN (1965) reported a method for the rapid determination of Ca, Mg, Na, K, and Fe in coal ash by atomic absorption which is similar to that described by BELCHER and BROOKS (1963). Determinations are carried out with preliminary separations using aliquot portions of the same ash solution. A 0.100 g sample of dried coal ash is placed in a platinum crucible and dissolved by a mixture of 3 ml of $HClO_4$ and 10 ml of HF. When the sample is completely dissolved, the HF is driven off and the sample diluted to 100 ml. The final dilution is such that 10 p.p.m. of metal in the solution corresponds to 1% of the element in the coal ash.

The calcium and magnesium solutions should be made up to contain one percent lanthanum to remove interference, especially that caused by aluminum (see Chapter 4). Sodium and potassium are determined with Osram lamps. The solutions as described are aspirated directly into an air-acetylene flame. Precision and accuracy for the method are in the range 1–3% (relative standard deviation).

CHAPTER 7

Rock and Mineral Analysis

To become routinely used for the analysis of trace elements in rocks and minerals, any instrumental method should possess several characteristics: (*1*) it must be simple in operation; (*2*) it must be sufficiently sensitive that chemical concentration prior to analysis is generally unnecessary; (*3*) it must be relatively interference free or adequate methods must be available for correction of interferences; (*4*) it must be rapid enough to allow large numbers of analyses to be run routinely; and (*5*) it must be precise and accurate. Of all the instrumentation techniques presently available, atomic absorption spectrometry is one method that satisfies all these requirements.

SILICATE ROCKS

While several early workers had applied the atomic absorption method to analysis of soils, BILLINGS (1963), TRENT and SLAVIN (1964b), and RAGLAND and BILLINGS (1965) were among the first to report studies of trace element content of silicate rocks by atomic absorption spectrometry. They determined the Ca, Mg, Na, K, Sr, Fe, and Mn contents in different silicate materials. The results obtained were similar regardless of whether the 0.5 g samples were put into solution with HF–H_2SO_4 treatment or were taken up in hot HCl after driving off any excess HF. Similarly, the fused samples were also taken up in HCl.

Data from TRENT and SLAVIN (1964b) for G-1 and W-1 are given in Table XX. G-1 is a granite from Westerly, Rhode Island, and W-1 is a diabase from Centerville, Virginia; these rocks are used internationally as geochemical standards.

TABLE XX

ANALYSIS OF G-1 AND W-1 STANDARDS (WEIGHT %)[1]

Element (as oxide)	*G-1*		*W-1*	
	FS[2]	*A.A.*	*FS*[1]	*A.A.*
Na_2O	3.32	3.42	2.07	2.25
K_2O	5.45	5.51	0.64	0.67
CaO	1.39	1.46	10.96	10.80
MgO	0.41	0.38	6.62	6.73
MnO	0.030	0.030	0.16	0.161
FeO (total reported as)	1.76	1.78	10.01	9.86
	1.75	1.93	2.50	2.10
Sr (p.p.m.)	280	243	220	190
	250	239	175	195

[1] After TRENT and SLAVIN (1964b); reproduced by courtesy of Perkin–Elmer Corp.
[2] Values given by FLEISCHER and STEVENS (1962).

In analyses for the alkaline earth metals, it is important that the acid content of sample and standards be matched. If the solids content exceeds 0.3%, a match of solids content between standards and samples is required to obtain 1% accuracy (TRENT and SLAVIN, 1964a). Strontium contents were also measured by dissolving 0.5 g samples of the standards G-1 and W-1 in HF–H_2SO_4 and sufficient lanthanum added to produce a 1% La solution in a final volume of 500 ml. Sodium was added to both sample and standards to remove any ionization effects. Strontium results, obtained by isotope dilution, X-ray fluorescence, and atomic absorption methods, agreed to within 3% for W-1 and 10% for G-1. Subsequently, TRENT and SLAVIN (1964c), analysed several National Bureau of Standard rock-like refractory materials. Those materials containing titanium, silicon, zirconium, and aluminum were dissolved by a combined HF–H_2SO_4 treatment and sodium carbonate fusion. The results for calcium and magnesium are given in Table XXI.

Sulfate was shown to produce an interference in the analysis for calcium. Lanthanum, however, can be used to control the interference of the sulfate radical. It is probably simpler, however, to use an acid other than sulfuric; HCl, HNO_3 and $HClO_4$ are all suitable.

Iron and manganese determinations made on the acid digests of the above noted silicate and refractory samples are also given in Table XXI. In general, the agreement between reported National

TABLE XXI

CALCIUM, MAGNESIUM, MANGANESE, AND IRON IN REFRACTORY MATERIALS (WEIGHT %)[1]

	CaO		*MnO*		*MgO*		*Fe_2O_3*	
Sample	*N.B.S.*	*A.A.*	*N.B.S.*	*A.A.*	*N.B.S.*	*A.A.*	*N.B.S.*	*A.A.*
N.B.S.-76 aluminum refractory	0.27	0.26	0.02	0.016	0.58	0.57	2.38	1.6
77	0.26	0.20	0.007	0.0026	0.50	0.37	0.90	0.79
78	0.38	0.26	0.005	0.0027	0.51	0.48	0.79	0.68
N.B.S.-102 silica brick	2.29	2.25	0.005	0.0039	0.21	0.178	0.66	0.65
198	2.71	2.63	0.008	0.0084	0.07	0.062	0.66	0.61
199	2.41	2.29	0.007	0.0068	0.13	0.125	0.74	0.73

[1] Modified from TRENT and SLAVIN (1964c), and SLAVIN (1965); reproduced by courtesy of Perkin–Elmer Corp.

Bureau of Standard values and those by atomic absorption is good. The techniques used by TRENT and SLAVIN (1964b, c) to achieve solution of the silicates are conventional ones. Both procedures can be used to prepare almost any silicate for flame analysis.

The HF–H_2SO_4 method for silicate sample preparation is straightforward. Place an accurately weighed portion (0.5 g is recommended) of the crushed (150 μ size) rock sample in a 30 ml platinum crucible. Add about 5 drops each of water and concentrated H_2SO_4 and follow with 5 ml of 50% HF. Place the crucible in a porcelain dish, place on a hot plate and heat slowly in a hood until all the H_2SO_4 has been fumed. When the sample is nearly dry repeat the procedure. Do this a third time to assure complete decomposition of the rock sample. Heat to complete dryness on the third evaporation. Transfer the metal sulfates to a 250 ml beaker with hot 1:9 HCl as needed. Transfer again to a 200 ml volumetric flask, cool and bring to the mark with 1:9 HCl. The solution is now ready to be analysed and can be aspirated directly into an air-acetylene flame. If a small residue results, other procedures are needed to dissolve the sample. These can be consulted in any standard textbook on quantitative chemistry (e.g., KOLTHOFF and SANDELL, 1952).

For the Na_2CO_3 fusion technique the procedure is as follows: Add an accurately weighed 0.5 g of crushed sample to a 30 ml platinum crucible. Weigh out about 4 g of pure, anhydrous Na_2CO_3 and add about 3 g to the crucible and stir with a glass rod until well mixed. Clean the glass rod with the remaining Na_2CO_3 and transfer the latter to the crucible. Place the covered crucible in a muffle furnace and heat until the crucible is dull red, hold this temperature for 10 min., then raise the temperature to 1,100°C for 60 min. Remove, place on asbestos boards and cool to room temperature with the cover on. The fused wafer can be removed whole by carefully squeezing the soft platinum crucible. Place the wafer in a 250 ml beaker and cover the wafer with approximately 100 ml of water. Slowly and carefully add 25 ml of concentrated HCl through a funnel set so its stem is under the water. Using the acid, wash the crucible cover so that the wash solution is added to the beaker. Heat the beaker gently until the wafer dissolves and then filter the contents into a 200 ml volumetric flask. Wash the beaker and filter paper repeatedly by adding the wash to the flask. Bring to the mark, analyse for the elements desired by aspirating the solution directly into the flame.

BELT (1964) determined the copper and zinc content in several types of silicate rocks, including W-1 and G-1, by direct analysis of acid digests of the rock. Precision for copper ranged from 34% at 5 p.p.m. to 3.3% at 210 p.p.m. in the sample; for zinc, the precision was better, ranging from 9.7% at 3 p.p.m. to 3.7% at 260 p.p.m. in the sample. The method is simple and direct. Dissolve approximately 0.5 g of rock sample in 5 ml of 48% HF and 1 ml of 70% $HClO_4$ in a Teflon* beaker and heat to 100°C until fuming ceases. Repeat the procedure and take up the resulting salts in two 3-ml portions of concentrated HCl. Heat if necessary to enhance the dissolution and then transfer to an appropriate sized flask (25 ml is adequate). Neutralize the acid solution with NH_4OH and bring to volume (25 ml). Aspirate the solution directly into an air-acetylene flame. Results obtained by this method are given in Table XXII. Various modifications of this procedure are possible;

TABLE XXII

COPPER AND ZINC ANALYSES OF DIFFERENT TYPES OF SILICATE ROCKS[1]

Rock types	Cu *(p.p.m.)*	Zn *(p.p.m.)*
tonalite	12	44
altered tonalite	104	151
altered porphyry	439	480
aplite	7	13
quartz monzanite	45	74
muscovite granite	14	16
hornblende quartz diorite	82	85
hornblende granodiorite	6.9	33
hornblende granodiorite	10	55
biotite quartz diorite	361	83
Silvermine granite	5	72
Graniteville granite	2.5	3.9
G-1	12	49
W-1	118	91

[1] Modified from BELT (1964). See original reference for sample locations. Used by permission of *Economic Geology*.

a simple one is to omit the neutralization step. In all the results on silicates, matrix effects were minimal. A similar procedure was used by RUBESKA and MOLDAN (1965).

It should be possible to use extraction techniques (see Chapter 5) employing ammonium pyrrolidine dithiocarbamate (APDC) as a chelating agent and methyl isobutyl ketone (MIBK) as an extract to determine copper, zinc, nickel, chromium, lead, cobalt, cadmium

* Registered trademark of the Du Pont Co.

and many other metals present in trace amounts in rock samples (SLAVIN, 1965). The metal can be extracted from the acid digest of the sample. Other workers (L. Wilson, quoted in: SLAVIN, 1965) have determined copper, zinc, lead and molybdenum at levels below 100 p.p.m. in rock samples by precipitating the metals from acid digests with thioacetamide.

BILLINGS and ADAMS (1964), RAGLAND and BILLINGS (1965) and BILLINGS (1965a) have determined a large number of elements in granites, spilites, andesites and other silicate materials. The samples were prepared by dissolving about 0.25 g of rock in an $HF–HNO_3$ mixture. Sufficient lanthanum nitrate was added to give the solutions a La/Al ratio > 10 to control interferences in the measurement of the alkaline earth metals and the final solution

TABLE XXIII

COMPARATIVE CHEMICAL DATA FOR FOUR TYPES OF IGNEOUS ROCKS. CONTENT IN WEIGHT PERCENT EXCEPT Rb (IN P.P.M.)[1]

Sample	*X-ray* Ca	*A.A.* Ca	*X-ray* Fe	*A.A.* Fe	*X-ray* Rb	*A.A.* Rb	*X-ray* K	*A.A.* K	*F.P.* K
Andesite	9.32	7.50	7.92	7.45	28	30	2.15	1.89	1.90
	4.75	4.05	5.90	4.41	24	29	1.81	1.54	–
	6.75	6.25	7.08	7.06	68	83	2.94	2.85	–
	5.24	5.20	6.82	5.67	23	19	1.54	1.32	–
Spilitized andesite	4.83	4.80	5.24	5.46	11	16	1.09	1.04	1.03
	5.12	5.00	4.90	4.69	17	10	0.96	0.67	0.90
	2.22	2.46	6.21	4.62	58	57	4.01	4.00	4.13
	1.63	2.06	4.44	3.64	74	60	3.26	3.26	3.45
Spilites	3.46	3.26	6.04	4.83	25	26	1.56	1.60	1.55
	8.22	7.10	8.17	7.20	25	28	1.14	1.00	1.04
	5.76	2.41	3.80	3.13	129	93	5.43	5.70	5.49
	10.70	7.80	6.67	6.57	33	31	1.92	1.80	1.87
Keratophyres	2.67	2.30	2.75	2.03	42	26	2.19	1.95	2.04
	0.55	0.66	1.88	2.80	–	–	2.25	2.25	2.21
	–	–	–	–	25	29	1.13	0.99	–

[1] Modified from BILLINGS (1965a); reproduced by courtesy of Perkin–Elmer Corp. A.A. = atomic absorption; F.P. = flame photometry.

brought up to 50 ml. Standards were prepared from G-1 and W-1. Table XXIII presents typical data for spilites, keratophyres, andesites, and spilitized andesites.

Mercury can be analysed at the 5 p.p.b. level in soils and rocks using the same method given in Chapter 6 (VAUGHN and McCARTHY, 1964). A lithium metaborate–nitric acid solution technique reported by INGAMELLS (1966) makes possible the analysis of most major and minor constituents of silicate rocks on a single sample. Carbon, hydrogen, and oxygen are excepted.

LAVAS

PERRAULT (1966) describes problems associated with the analyses of lavas for Cu and Zn, and Ni. The samples were put into solution using a conventional HF treatment. It was critical that the standards and samples be prepared in a similar fashion to prevent the introduction of considerable error into the results obtained. Absorption at a given elemental concentration differs depending upon the acids used (HNO_3, HCl, H_2SO_4, HF or $HClO_4$) in preparing the standards and samples.

In an investigation of deuteric alteration within large ignimbrite sheets SCOTT (1966) used atomic absorption to analyse for Na, K, Ca, Mg and Fe. No details on the technique were given but several of the methods discussed herein could be used for such studies.

SILICATE MINERALS

The application of atomic absorption to mineral analyses has been incompletely investigated as yet. BILLINGS (1964), BILLINGS and ADAMS (1964), and RAGLAND and BILLINGS (1965) reported on the study of cadmium, nickel, cobalt, rubidium, iron, strontium, potassium, sodium, and calcium in biotite, plagioclase, and alkali feldspars.

Sample preparation is quite simple. Dissolve approximately 0.25 gram of the rock mineral sample (–200 mesh) to be studied in 50 ml of HF and 20 ml HNO_3 and dry by heat lamp evaporation in a Teflon beaker. Upon dryness, add 2 ml HCl and 25 ml H_2O. Add 0.5 ml concentrated NH_4OH and sufficient lanthanum nitrate to make the La/Al ratio > 10. Transfer the solution to a 50 ml volumetric flask and bring the final solutions to 50 ml. Known silicon, aluminum, and phosphorus interferents are removed; the silicon as S F_4 by the HF treatment, the aluminum by buffering with lanthanum. Phosphorus is present in too low an amount to result in serious interference. For details on removal of specific interferences see Chapter 4. The lithium metaborate-nitric acid method (INGAMELLS, 1966) noted earlier is also applicable to studies of the major and minor element content of silicate minerals.

Sensitivity and precision for some elements are given in Table XXIV. Typical values for the same elements are shown in Table XXV.

Accuracy tests have adequately shown that atomic absorption

TABLE XXIV

PRECISION AND SENSITIVITY IN MINERAL SAMPLES[1]

Element	*Sample*	*Precision*[2]	*Sensitivity*[3]
Ca	plagioclase and K-feldspar	4	10
Ca	biotite	2	10
Fe	K-feldspar	2.5	20
Fe	biotite	1	–
K	plagioclase and K-feldspar	5	1
K	biotite	1	1
Na	plagioclase and K-feldspar	1	1.5
Na	biotite	2	1
Rb	plagioclase and K-feldspar	1.5	2
Rb	biotite	1	2
Sr	plagioclase and K-feldspar	1.5	25
Sr	biotite	3	10
Cd	biotite	15	0.4
Co	biotite	7	2
Ni	biotite	7	2

[1] Modified from RAGLAND and BILLINGS (1965) and BILLINGS and ADAMS (1964)
[2] $\pm$ % of the amount present.
[3] In p.p.m. in the rock sample.

TABLE XXV

TYPICAL ELEMENTAL VALUES OF ROCK MINERALS (AS % OF ROCK SAMPLES)[1]

Mineral	*Ca*	*Fe*	*K*	*Na*	*Rb*	*Sr*
plagioclase feldspar	0.45	0.030	0.76	8.1	<0.0015	0.21
Nepheline	0.41	0.044	4.5	10.0	0.0098	0.029
K-feldspar	0.31	0.06	7.0	4.38	0.0119	0.032

[1] Modified from BILLINGS and ADAMS (1964); reproduced by courtesy of Perkin–Elmer Corp.

compares well to standard chemical methods of silicate analysis. Results for specific elements obtained by X-ray fluorescence, colorimetry, flame photometry, and other methods when compared with atomic absorption generally agreed within 10%.

TRACE METALS IN QUARTZ AND JASPEROID

Few analyses of the trace element content of quartz are available. PRICE and RAGLAND (1966a), however, desciibe a method for making such analyses. Quartz samples are ground to pass a 100 mesh (150 μ screen) and the –100 + 200 mesh fraction is retained. This fraction is washed with water and a pure quartz separate obtained by using heavy liquid (bromoform) and magnetic separations. A 0.5 g of sample is weighed out in a Teflon beaker and approximately 30 ml of a 3:1 HF–HNO_3 acid mixture added. The exact amount or ratio is not critical. Allow the sample to digest overnight with covers on, under heat lamps. Subsequently, the covers are removed and the solution evaporated to dryness. Moisten the sample with a few drops of HNO_3 and take the solution up in 10 ml water and bring to a boil. When boiling starts, remove from the heat, allow the sample to cool to room temperature, and dilute the sample to volume in a 50 ml volumetric flask. Standards can be prepared using appropriate reagent salts.

Using this technique and an air-acetylene flame, PRICE and RAGLAND (1966a) studied the content of Li, Zn, Cu, Ag, Au, and

Fe in pure quartz from several localities. Data are presented in Table XXVI. It should be emphasized that the data in Table XXVI are atypical. They are much higher than usual values for pure quartz–probably due to minute inclusions. The authors were looking for a prospecting tool. These values are from gold and silver bearing veins.

TABLE XXVI

TRACE ELEMENTS IN QUARTZ (IN P.P.M.)[1]

Sample	*Zn*	*Cu*	*Ag*	*Au*	*Li*	*Fe*
1	15.9	10.4	7.7	1.7	0.24	1420
3	7.3	33.1	<0.8	<1.7	<0.08	2020
5	18.0	138.0	6.3	12.6	0.08	1180
7	13.8	30.4	1.0	<2.1	0.74	2560
9	1.4	9.5	<1.2	3.0	<0.12	2620
11	1.6	5.7	2.0	<1.9	0.18	230
13	0.6	2.7	0.15	3.5	2.16	32

[1] Condensed from Price and Ragland (1966a).

LOVERING et al. (1966) used the atomic absorption technique described by VAUGHN and MCCARTHY (1964) to study the mercury content of 93 samples of jasperoid and chert. The purpose was to tets the significance of mercury as one criterion for recognizing metalliferous ore-associated jasperoid bodies. A detection limit of 0.01 p.p.m. mercury was claimed. The precision of analysis in the mercury range studied (0.02–90 p.p.m.) was ± 20%. The samples were from several different districts and mineralized areas, including such famous areas as Gilman, Leadville, and Uncompahgre in Colorado; Santa Rita, New Mexico; Tintic, Bingham and Vernon, Utah; and others.

SULFIDE MINERALS

A direct method for the determination of silver in the minerals galena, tetrahedrite, sphalerite and antimonides is described in RUBESKA et al. (1967). The minerals are decomposed by nitric acid and/or sulfuric acid. Tartaric acid is added to prevent precipitation of antimonic acid. The determination is relatively interference free. Results are in general agreement with those found by the fire assay, however, the results by atomic absorption were some 1–10% higher. Several other elements can be determined in the same solution which extends an opportunity for needed trace element studies of the named and similar sulfide minerals.

LIMESTONES

The major and trace element content of limestones can be determined quite simply by atomic absorption If the elemental content of the carbonate fraction is of interest, it is only necessary to acidify the sample and aspirate the acidized fraction. Standard solutions should, of course, have the same viscosity as the samples. Use of the addition method obviates the viscosity problem.

Samples of 1–2g are usually adequate. The amount will vary depending upon the amount of carbonate making up the sample. The sample is placed in a 200 ml flask and 50 ml of either 0.1 *N* HCl or acetic acid added to dissolve the sample. The latter lessens damage to any included clays, if they are to be analysed in a later step.

If additional acid is required, it is added until effervescence ceases. The solution is then brought to 200 ml with distilled or deionized water. This solution can be aspirated directly into the flame.

If a total analysis of the limestone is desired, the method of TRENT and SLAVIN (1964a) can be used. A 0.5 g limestone sample is heated in a platinum crucible in a muffle furnace for 1,100°C for 1 h. After cooling, place the sample in Teflon beakers and treat the sample with 5 drops of concentrated H_2SO_4 and 5 ml of HF. Warm until fumes of sulfur trioxide are evolved, repeat. The residue can be taken up in 1:9 HCl, then dilute to 100 ml with 1:9 HCl. Table XXVII compares results obtained by this method with those given for National Bureau of Standards limestone samples 1A and 88 (a dolomite).

TABLE XXVII

COMPARISON OF ATOMIC ABSORPTION RESULTS WITH NATIONAL BUREAU OF STANDARDS REPORTED VALUES FOR 1A AND 88 (DOLOMITE) (IN %)[1]

N.B.S. material	*CaO*		*MgO*		*MnO*		*Fe_2O_3*	
	N.B.S.	*A.A.*	*N.B.S.*	*A.A.*	*N.B.S.*	*A.A.*	*N.B.S.*	*A.A.*
Limestone 1A	Ave 41.3	42.3	2.19	2.03	0.038	0.038	1.63	1.63
Limestone 88	Ave 30.5	29.4	21.5	20.5	0.01	0.0075	0.086	0.081

[1] Modified from TRENT and SLAVIN (1964a).

For lime materials, dissolve 0.5 g of material in H_2SO_4 and HF in Teflon beakers and dilute to 100 ml in 1:9 HCl, filter off insoluble materials and analyse for the desired element, using appropriate instrument settings. If desired, the samples can be stored in polyethylene or polypropylene bottles.

Another approach for total sample analysis involves the hydration of SiO_2 with perchloric acid (E. E. Angino and O. K. Galle, unpublished data) which is then filtered off leaving the Ca and Mg and R_2O_3 group in solution.

In working with carbonates it is extremely important that the solution used to make working curves be made with the same acid used to put the samples into solution. Standards made up with HCl, HNO_3, and $HClO_4$ will produce three different curves. Nitric acid provides the least sensitivity, HCl is next, and $HClO_4$ produces highest sensitivity.

The results of an accuracy test for calcium in carbonate rocks is given in Table XXVIII. An air-acetylene flame was employed for these tests (BILLINGS, 1965a). Generally the results agree within 5%.

RUBESKA et al. (1963) reported a method for determination of Na in limestone. Their method is as follows: Dissolve 5 g of sample in 20 ml of redistilled HCl, boil and filter the solution. Save the filtrate. Ignite the undissolved portion and treat with 0.5 ml of $HClO_4$ and 1 ml of HF in a platinum crucible within a Teflon beaker. After evaporation, dissolve the residue in 3 ml of 1:4 HCl and add to the filtrate. Place in a 100 ml volumetric flask and make up to volume. Aspirate this sample directly into the flame. Interferences to be

TABLE XXVIII

CALCIUM IN CARBONATE ROCKS (WEIGHT % Ca)[1]

Sample	*X-ray fluorescence*	*Atomic absorption*
Ys-13	38.0	37.7
Ys-20	23.2	21.5
Sa-10	38.2	38.5
M-1	39.1	37.7
C-1	39.3	39.5
R-1	33.5	33.8
Y-1	22.4	20.4
R-2	29.6	30.2
Q-1	17.3	16.6

[1] Condensed from BILLINGS (1965a).

expected for this rock type were discussed earlier. A sensitivity of 0.15 p.p.m. Na was reported. Relative deviation for the range 0.001–0.07% sodium was 4.7%. A similar method for the determination of magnesium in carbonate rocks is given in RUBESKA and MOLDAN (1965).

As is obvious, the analyses of the trace metallic content of rocks and minerals by atomic absorption is a relatively simple matter. Although we have discussed the procedures used for only a few of the many known rock and mineral species, it should be apparent that only minor modifications, if any, of the methods described are needed to analyse almost any of the silicate rocks and minerals by this method.

Trace metal analysis of carbonate and dolomite rocks is simple as they are easily put into a form (solution) suitable for analysis. The use of atomic absorption spectroscopy in the study of trace and major element distribution in geologic material promises to expand at a rapid rate.

CHAPTER 8

Recent Sediments

The increased interest in all phases of marine geochemistry has stimulated investigations of the trace metal content of the different types of recent marine sediments. Many of these types of samples (e.g., recent carbonates, silty sediments) can be prepared for analysis by atomic absorption using the methods outlined in other chapters; often, however, the normal methods may require considerable modification before they can be used routinely. Therefore, preparative schemes for atomic absorption analysis of recent sediments are presented separately.

Considerable interest exists in the composition of different fractions (carbonate, detrital, etc.) that make up the sediment material. The methods described can be used to study any of the fractions of the sediment desired or the total sediment.

TOTAL SEDIMENT ANALYSIS AND SILTY SEDIMENTS

ANGINO (1965) describes a simple technique for determining the trace element content (Fe, Mn, Ni, Co, Mo, Zn) of various fractions (carbonate, silicate, organic, etc.) of recent sediments. Prepare standard solutions of the elements to be studied to cover the desired concentration range. Grind approximately 5 g samples in a mortar and pestle to pass a 60 mesh (250 μ) screen, and place 1–2 g of the sample in small Teflon beakers. Teflon beakers of approximately 30 ml capacity can be made by cutting 2-inch lengths from a 5 ft., 2-inch diameter Teflon rod and turning down the inside on a lathe.

To the 1–2 g sample, add 5 ml of 48% HF and 5 drops of concentrated H_2SO_4. Add the latter slowly to prevent foaming of the HF solution. Place beakers on a hot plate and heat at 100°C to dryness. Repeat the above steps twice. After the third drying step, transfer the solute to a 250 ml Erlenmeyer flask using 200 ml of hot 9:1 v/v HCl. Add the hot HCl in 20–30 ml portions with stirring and crushing of the metallic sulfates, using a stirring rod.

In some instances all the solute will not dissolve and a black residue will remain. This can be taken up in H_2O_2 using the following technique: filter the HCl solution into a second flask. Place the filter paper in a 100 ml beaker and wash the paper with 20 ml of distilled, demineralized water and 20 ml of 30% H_2O_2. Heat the solution slightly and the black residue (organic in nature) dissolves readily. Combine the two solutions, determine the total volume and analyse for the desired trace elements by aspirating directly into an air-acetylene flame (ANGINO, 1967). D. A. Dobbins (personal communication, 1966) used the atomic absorption method in an investigation of the K, Ca, Na, and Mg content of samples of fine grained, principally silty and clay sized sediments from the Pamlico River–Pamlico Sound, North Carolina estuarine environment. Samples of fine-grained, principally silt and clay-sized, sediment were collected from the middle of the River and Sound using a Phleger corer. Cores were extruded from their plastic tubes and cut into 8 cm long sections which were sealed in small glass bottles with toluene to prevent bacterial metabolism. At each station, surface and bottom water samples were collected and stored in polyethylene bottles.

In the laboratory the water samples were acidified with glacial acetic acid and formaldehyde added to prevent bacterial growth. The water was then filtered (0.45 μ millipore) diluted 100- to 1,000-fold with distilled water, and analysed for Na, K, Ca, and Mg on a Perkin–Elmer Model 303 instrument.

The mud core samples were removed from the toluene-filled bottles, trimmed to remove any disturbed mud. A 12 ml slice was placed in a 5.5 cm Buchner funnel with Whatman # 40 filter paper for suction filtration to remove the pore water. The extracted water was taken up in a hypodermic syringe, put into an appropriate container and diluted to 50 ml. This was followed by a 20-fold dilution prior to analysis.

Finally, to determine the exchangeable cations, a 1–2 g piece (wet) of the filter cake was washed with methanol to remove any dissolved cations remaining in the pores of the sediment. Subsequently, 1 *N* NH_4 OAc (ammonium acetate) (pH 7) was added and intimately mixed with the sediment and the mixture centrifuged according to the procedure given in JACKSON (1958, p.86). The supernatant (60 ml) was then diluted to 100 ml. Prior to analysis a further 10-fold dilution was made.

All the solutions were checked for chemical interferences by the single sample standard addition method (i.e., the "spike" method), but none were observed and no correction was applied to the raw data.

CARBONATE, ORGANIC-RICH AND LEACHED SEDIMENTS

If one desires an elemental analysis of a specific type of sediment such as carbonate, organic rich and/or leached sediments, the methods described below are applicable. Place 1–2 g of crushed sample (250 μ) in a 150 ml beaker, and slowly add 75 ml 9:1 v/v water/HCl until effervescence ceases. While stirring, add another 25 ml of the acid, let the solution stand for 15 min. Transfer the solution to an appropriate container and analyse for the desired elements by aspirating directly into an air-hydrogen or air-acetylene flame. Refractory elements such as aluminum require a hotter flame (O_2–H_2, oxyacetylene, or nitrous oxide-acetylene) (E. E. Angino and M. Baird, unpublished data).

In studies of carbonate sediments or of the carbonate fraction of silty sediments a 9:1 v/v acetic acid solution can be used in place of the HCl to reduce leaching from any clay minerals present. The procedure is the same except the sample should be allowed to set for 2–3 h prior to separation of the supernatant.

For examination of the organic fraction, add either 75 ml of 10% H_2O_2 or 100 ml of chlorox solution to 1–2 g of crushed (250 μ)

sample in a 150 ml beaker and let sit for 4 h with occasional stirring. This solution can be aspirated directly into the flame. The H_2O_2 solution is preferred as clogging of laminar flow burners commonly occurs with the use of a chlorox solution. Chlorox can also contaminate the sample for several cations. However, H_2O_2 often contains PO_4 which may complex the alkaline earths. The complexing effect, if present, may be reduced by a La buffer addition or by using standards containing PO_4. A blank should be analysed to determine the contamination from chlorox or hydrogen peroxide.

A "leached fraction" can be examined by washing 1–2 g of ground sediment in a 150 ml beaker with 100 ml of distilled deionized water with constant stirring for 4 h. Allow the solution to sit for 12 h. Separate the supernatant solution by centrifugation or vacuum-filtration for the desired elements.

Interferences in carbonate sediments are minor. For some elements (e.g., Fe, Co, Ni) calcium interference (molecular absorption) is sometimes noted, especially at lower flame temperatures and with a laminar flow burner. This interference is most noticeable in studying either the carbonate fraction of sediments or carbonate rich sediment themselves. Correction for this interference is easily applied and is described in the chapter on interferences.

Another approach to preparing carbonate rich sediments is described by J. Watson and E. E. Angino (unpublished data) in a study of iron-rich sediments from the Gulf of Mexico. The samples are air dried and then ground in a mortar and pestle to pass a 60 mesh (250 μ) screen. A 3.0 g sample is placed in a weighed 250 ml Erlenmeyer flask and 20 ml distilled water added. Add 80 ml of 0.1 *M* sodium acetate buffered to pH 3.7 with acetic acid. The sample is stirred occasionally and allowed to set for 24 h. After heating to 60°C briefly, the pH again is measured. If the pH rises appreciably, some Ca CO_3 is assumed still present. Add 50 ml NaAc and repeat the procedure until the pH increase does not exceed 0.1. Separate the insoluble fraction and analyze the filtrate directly for the desired elements.

G. K. Billings and P. C. Ragland (unpublished data) have determined Mn, Fe, Cr, Co, Ni, Rb, Na, K, Li, Zn, Mg, Ca, and

Sr, in modern marine carbonates. The only interference was Ca molecular absorption. The method consisted of dissolving a 2 g sample (–200 mesh $\simeq$ 74 μ) in 25 ml of 1*N* HCl for 2 min. in an ultrasonic bath, filtering the solution through a 0.45 μ filter into a 100 ml volumetric flask and diluting to volume. This solution is aspirated directly into the flame. This method will also strip some of the absorbed cations from the clays.

SKELETAL MATERIALS

HARRISS and ALMY (1964) determined Fe, K, Mg, Mn, Na, and Sr in scleractinian corals (*Acropora cervicornis* (LAMARCK), *A. palmata* (LAMARCK) and *Porites Porites* var. *furcata* (LAMARCK) by atomic absorption. The technique consisted of cleaning the specimens thoroughly in distilled water and grinding manually in a ceramic mortar to a fine powder. A 0.25 g sample of each specimen was dissolved in 0.6 *N* acetic acid and aspirated directly into the flame. The precision was good. HARRISS (1964) used the same technique in his study of the transfer of strontium, iron, and magnesium from sea water to the skeletal carbonate material of *Balanus eburnesis* GOULD, *Littorina irrorata* SAY, and *Crossostrea virginica* GEMLIN; a barnacle, gastropod, and pelecypod respectively.

ORGANIC FRACTIONS OF RECENT SEDIMENTS

Many of the common organic solvents can be used in conjunction with atomic absorption to accurately investigate the trace element content of the organic fractions of recent sediments. BURRELL (1965c) described a method for metal determination of the asphaltic fraction of recent sediments. The technique consists of treating dry sediments with chloroform. Subsequently, the lipid fraction of the dissolved organic material is removed with petroleum ether and the remaining chloroform fraction contains the "defined" asphaltic material. Methanol is added in small increments to the chloroform solution until a mixture is obtained which gives a suitable flame for analysis and at the same time keeps the asphaltic fraction in solution. The solution is unstable and organics are precipitated after standing for some time.

Standards were prepared by adding 1 ml of aqueous standards to 5 ml of a 3:2 methanol–chloroform mixture. Detection limits and sensitivities of this method are given in Table XXIX. Similar results were obtained using either aqueous or 2-propanol solvents.

TABLE XXIX

DETECTION (p.p.m.) AND SENSITIVITIES (P.P.M. FOR 1% ABSORPTION) USING METHANOL CHLOROFORM[1]

Element	*Detection limit*	*Sensitivity*
Cobalt	0.05	0.10
Nickel	0.10	0.20
Iron	0.15	0.25

[1] Modified from BURRELL (1965a); reproduced by courtesy of Perkin–Elmer Corp.

Many other simple means exist for preparing recent marine sediments for trace metal analyses by atomic absorption spectroscopy. Those presented here are typical and illustrate the basic simplicity of the method. They will serve as a starting point for the many modifications that will be used to satisfy the different instrumentation and sample requirements.

CHAPTER 9

Isotopes and Noble Gases

Comparatively few studies have been reported on the use of atomic absorption techniques for isotopic abundance studies, even though the possibility was noted early (WALSH, 1955).

It can be shown that the emission lines from a hollow cathode source have a band width of 0.01–0.04 Å. Atomic absorption can be used for isotopic analysis provided that the isotopic spectral displacement for an element is greater than the spectral band widths obtained with the emission source. Table XXX from MANNING and SLAVIN (1962) lists the isotope shifts for the principal absorption lines of some elements. Only those elements at each end of the periodic table have adequate spectral separations for isotopic analysis by atomic absorption using present methods and techniques.

LITHIUM ISOTOPES

ZAIDEL and KORENNOI (1961) and MANNING and SLAVIN (1962) in their study of lithium isotopes were first to apply the method of atomic absorption spectrometry to isotopic investigations. Both groups used flames as light sources. The former investigators gave no results of the natural $^7Li/^6Li$ ratio and the latter's results were of a preliminary nature. However, GOLEB and YOKAYAMA (1964), using atomic absorption, determined the ratio of $^7Li/^6Li$ in a sample of LiOH to be 12.1 ± 3.3%, in excellent agreement with the mass spectrometer value of 12.3 used by the Oak Ridge Isotope Division for reporting the lithium isotope abundance.

TABLE XXX

ISOTOPE SHIFTS[1]

Metal	*Isotopes*	*Resonance line (Å)*	*Δ λ (Å)*
Li	6,7	6,708	0.15
B	10,11	2,498	0.02
Mg	24,25	2,852	0.002
	24,26		0.004
K	39,41	7,665	0.004
Cu	63,65	3,247	0.002
Zn	64,66	2,139	0.0007
	64,68	2,139	0.0014
Sr	84,86	4,607	0.001
	84,88	4,607	0.002
Rb	85,87	7,800	0.001
Zr	90,96		0.006
Mo	92,100		0.03
Ag	107,109	3,281	0.002
Ba	138,134	5,535	0.005
Hg	202,198	2,537	0.02
ThII	232,230		0.1
UII	238,236	4,244	0.15
	238,235	4,244	0.25
	238,234	4,244	0.30
	238,233	4,244	0.40

[1] Modified from MANNING and SLAVIN (1962); reproduced by courtesy of Perkin–Elmer Corp.

Experimental techniques

Because of the large isotope displacement of 0.15 Å the lithium doublet at 6,708 Å was selected by the referenced investigators. For lithium isotopes, at 6,708 Å, the two lines of each isotope's spectrum are separated by 0.15 Å, which is equal to the shift between the two spectra. As a result, the strong ^{6}Li line is superimposed on the weak line of ^{7}Li. This means it is impossible to make absorption measurements of one isotope free from the effects of the other when using mixed sources. Using enriched ^{6}Li or ^{7}Li sources, it is possible to measure the absorption of a sample using first one isotope and then the other as a source. The ratio of the two absorptions can then be used to establish a working curve for an analysis (Fig.11).

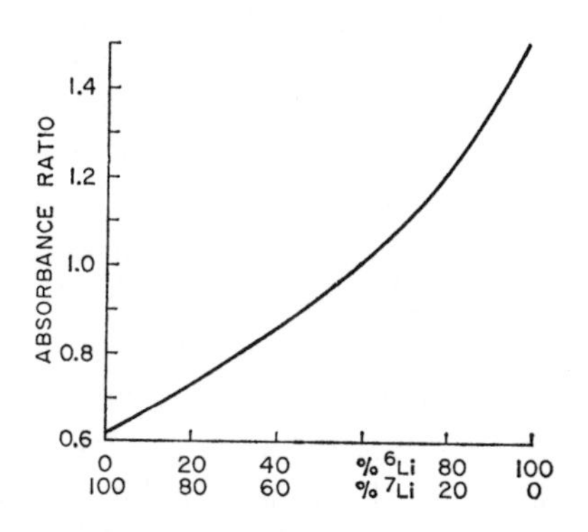

Fig.11. Working curve based on the absorbance ratios of lithium isotopes. (After MANNING and SLAVIN, 1962; by courtesy of Perkin–Elmer Corp.)

GOLEB and YOKAYAMA (1964) prepared standards by dissolving high purity ^{6}Li and ^{7}Li metals in distilled water. The resulting ^{6}Li and ^{7}Li solutions were used to prepare standards for the absorption tube. Two standard water solutions were made up containing the respective isotopes. Subsequently, from these two solutions, four secondary standards covering a range of 2.5–10.0 atomic percent ^{6}Li in ^{7}Li were prepared to establish a working curve. Respective ^{6}Li and ^{7}Li absorption readings were obtained for the four standards by passing ^{6}Li and ^{7}Li incident light independently through the discharge of the absorption tube containing the standards. A working curve was obtained by plotting log (I_6/I_{06})/log (I_7/I_{07}) against ^{6}Li concentration, where I_{06} and I_{07} are the respective ^{6}Li and ^{7}Li incident intensities and I_6 and I_7 are the respective transmitted intensities. An additional plot of I_6/I_{06} against ^{6}Li concentration for the standards also gave a straight line and coincided with a Li analytical curve predicted by ZAIDEL and KORENNOI (1961) for the appropriate absorption coefficient (0.425). Using similar techniques it should be possible to measure the lithium isotopic ratio found in natural materials.

URANIUM ISOTOPES

Goleb (1966c) describes two methods for measuring the uranium isotope masses 235 and 238 quantitatively and simply by atomic absorption: (*1*) the sample and standards are placed in an absorption tube in a conventional manner; (*2*) the sample and standards are used in the emission tube, the absorption tube carrying a relatively pure sample of the isotope to be determined. We will refer to these methods as the conventional and emission tube methods, respectively. A water-cooled hollow cathode discharge tube was used as an absorption tube. Large numbers of uranium atoms in the ground state were produced by the discharge in the tube. Thus the weak uranium resonance radiation coming from an emission source and passing through the absorption tube was absorbed. For the first time in an atomic absorption study, Goleb reversed the normal procedure and instead used samples and related standards in the emission source instead of in the absorption source. Good accuracy and precision were reported. Valid results were also obtained by the conventional approach: i.e., samples and related standards were employed in the absorption source. Table XXXI gives some results obtained using Goleb's technique (Goleb, 1966c).

Goleb (1963) initially used the uranium 3,915.4 Å line; however, later studies indicated that this line was of limited value for uranium isotope work.

Analysis of uranium isotopes is complicated by analytical difficulties such as flame temperature and nondissociation in a conventional flame.

Two reasons exist for using uranium samples and related standards in the emission source rather than the absorption source: (*1*) chips, oxides, etc., can be used to enhance the ground state population of uranium atoms, thus obviating the problem of dissolving refractory uranium; (*2*) greater freedom is possible with emission sources than absorption sources because the proportion of incident light absorbed is independent of emission intensity. Emission source refers to the sample and standards being used in

TABLE XXXI

URANIUM-238 ATOM %[1]

Sample no.	*Atomic absorption*	*Mass spectrometry*	*Deviation (atom %)*	*Relative deviation (%)*
(*1*) 50 (mg) metal	78.8	79.7	0.90	1.1
(*2*) 50 (mg) metal	60.3	59.9	0.40	0.7
(*3*) 50 (mg) metal	51.5	50.4	1.10	2.2
(*4*) 50 (mg) metal	40.6	39.5	1.10	2.8
(*5*) 50 (mg) metal	19.6	19.1	0.50	2.6
(*6*) 50 (mg) metal	5.60	5.59	0.01	0.2
(*7*) 50 (mg) U_3O_8	49.8	50.4	0.60	1.2
(*8*) 36 (mg) U_3O_8 (92 atom % U-236)	2.41	2.38	0.03	1.3
(*9*) 1 (mg) uranyl nitrate (98 atom % U-234)	0.58	0.60	0.02	3.3

[1] From GOLEB (1966c); reproduced by permission from *Anal. Chim. Acta.*

an emission tube, the absorption tube carrying a relatively pure sample of the isotope to be determined.

In a subsequent study GOLEB (1966c) used the 4,153 Å and 5,027 Å lines of uranium for isotopic studies because: (*1*) the isotope shift is larger than 0.05 Å (about 0.07 and 0.10 Å, respectively); and (*2*) the ^{235}U component of the 4,153 Å and 5,027 Å lines appear to have only a small hyperfine structure, consequently minimum interference is expected between ^{235}U and its related isotopes.

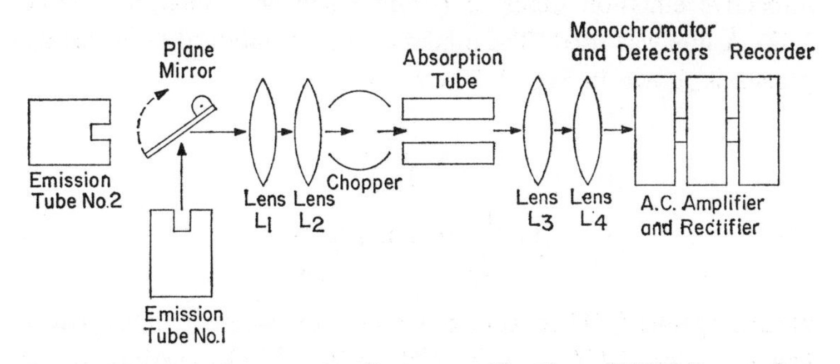

Fig.12. Schematic diagram of equipment used by GOLEB (1966c) for uranium isotopes by atomic absorption.

Using the equipment shown in Fig.12, the ratio $^{238}U/^{235}U$ can be determined accurately. A sample containing atoms of mass ^{238}U and ^{235}U is placed in the absorption tube; the two emission tubes contain ^{235}U and ^{238}U, respectively.

From light absorption theory, it can be shown that:

$$I_{238} = I^{\circ}_{238}\, e - \alpha L C_{238}$$

or

$$\ln \frac{I^{\circ}_{238}}{I_{238}} = \alpha L C_{238} \qquad (1)$$

where I_{238} and I^{0}_{238} are transmitted and incident light intensities respectively for ^{238}U, α is absorptivity coefficient for a single spectral line, L is length of absorption tube, and C_{238} is the concentration.

Similarly for ^{235}U. If α is the same for the two isotopes, then:

$$\frac{\ln I^{\circ}_{238}/I_{238}}{\ln I^{\circ}_{235}/I_{235}} = C_{238}/C_{235} \qquad (2)$$

This ratio can be determined independently of α and L, if L remains constant, while the absorption measurement can be obtained for the two emission tubes rapidly.

For the determination of ^{235}U and ^{238}U by the conventional method, samples and related standards are used sequentially in the absorption tube. Uranium metal depleted in ^{235}U (99.8 atom % ^{238}U) and purified ^{235}U (94.6 atom % ^{235}U) were used in the respective emission tubes to obtain resonance radiation. The U 3,027 Å line was used. The analytical curve obtained with this approach is shown in Fig.13. The ratio:

$$\frac{\log \dfrac{I^{\circ}_{235}}{I_{235}}}{\log \dfrac{I^{\circ}_{235}}{I_{235}} + \log \dfrac{I^{\circ}_{238}}{I_{238}}} \qquad (3)$$

plotted against ^{235}U concentration gave an essentially linear curve. Owing to the 5.4% atom % ^{238}U in the ^{235}U emission source, the curve does not pass through zero.

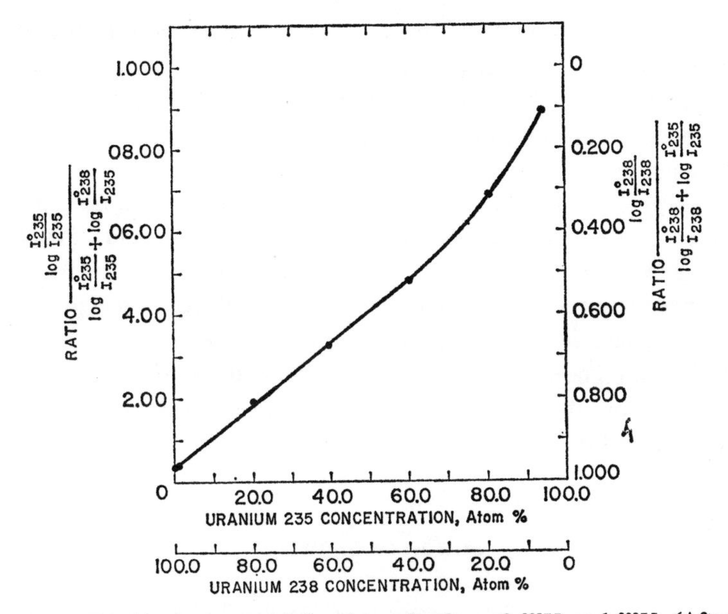

Fig.13. Working curve used for determination of ^{235}U and ^{238}U. (After GOLEB, 1966c; by permission of *Anal. Chim. Acta.*)

For the emission tube method, the samples for analysis can be in one emission tube and a single isotope used in both the other emission and absorption tube. The technique was tested using both ^{238}U and ^{235}U. Table XXXII shows comparison of results using the emission tube method and mass spectrographic results. Samples analysed were in the forms of metal, oxide, and salts.

TABLE XXXII

URANIUM-235 ATOM %[1]

Sample No.	*Atomic absorption*	*Mass Spectrometry*	*Deviation (atom %)*	*Relative deviation (%)*
1	3.00	3.05	0.05	1.6
2	20.3	20.1	0.2	1.0
3*	94.6	94.7	0.1	0.1

[1] From GOLEB (1966c); reproduced by permission from *Anal. Chim. Acta.*
* Sample is an alloy of 80% thorium and 20% enriched uranium metal.

In the last two samples, ^{238}U was determined in the presence of ^{235}U and ^{236}U, respectively. It thus appears that in working with ^{235}U, the ^{234}U, ^{236}U, and ^{238}U components of the 4,153 Å U line do not interfere with the ^{235}U component.

A number of uranium samples were analysed for uranium isotopes by sputtering samples and related standards in the absorption tube in the technique described by GOLEB (1963 and 1966c). Table XXXII is a comparison of atomic absorption and mass spectrometer results. Sufficient atoms were produced in the ground state (in sample 3) to determine uranium isotopes in the presence of thorium. The extension of these techniques to investigate uranium and possibly thorium isotopic fractionation, in geologic material seems possible.

BORON ISOTOPES

Later GOLEB (1966d) reported on the feasibility of measuring the natural abundance ratio for the boron isotopes $^{11}B/^{10}B$ using atomic absorption spectrophotometry (A.A.S.). The two boron lines used were the strong resonance lines at 2,496 and 2,497 Å. Isotope displacement for these two lines is about 0.02 Å. If the half-width of these boron lines is equal to or smaller than their isotope displacement, isotope determinations can be made. Preliminary results, however, suggest the determination of natural abundance ratios for boron isotopes by atomic absorption is not possible.

The sensitivity for an element of interest by A.A.S. is dependent on the shape of the spectral emission line. In the absence of self-absorption in the hollow-cathode tube, the strong boron line has twice the intensity of the weak boron lines. Consequently, if instrument current is plotted against the intensity ratio B-2,497.7/B-2,496.8 (Fig.14) a straight line can be drawn parallel to the abscissa for a range of intensities.

Goleb attempted several experiments using ^{10}B and ^{11}B (in amorphous form) in separate emission tubes. When light from

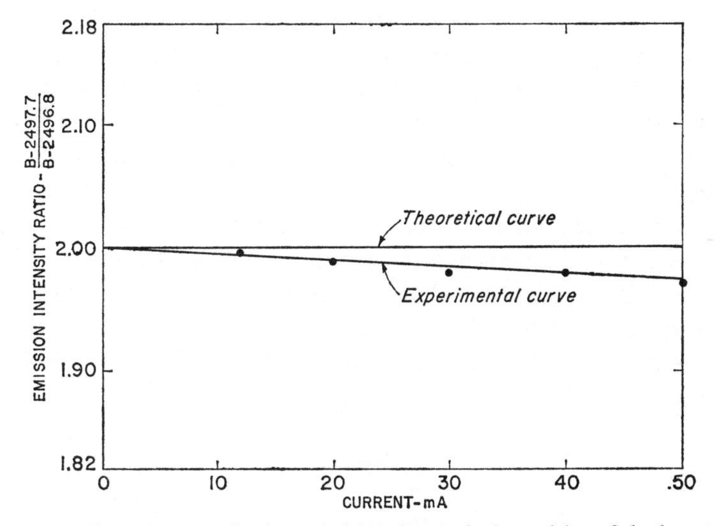

Fig.14. Effect of current in the emission tube on the intensities of the boron lines. (After GOLEB, 1966d; by permission of *Anal. Chim. Acta.*

^{10}B and ^{11}B sources respectively were passed through the active absorption tube containing normal amorphous boron, approximately the same amount of ^{10}B and ^{11}B light was absorbed. The transmitted intensities of ^{10}B and ^{11}B were essentially the same, even though there was approximately four times more ^{11}B than ^{10}B in the absorption tube. It appears, therefore, that the determination of boron isotopic ratios in natural materials is not presently possible by atomic absorption. It may be possible with the use of high temperature (N_2O–H_2; O_2–H_2) flames, but to date no work has been reported.

MERCURY ISOTOPES

A simple method for the determination of the percentage of ^{202}Hg present in small samples of mercury is described by OSBORN and GUNNING (1955). An electrodeless discharge tube containing ^{202}Hg is used as a source for the ^{202} Hg hyperfine component of the

2,537 Å resonance line of mercury. From measurements of the absorbance of this component by mercury vapor, the quantity of the isotope present in the vapor can be determined. Analyses of mercury samples containing different percentages of ^{202}Hg agree within three percent with values obtained by mass spectrometry.

Osborn and Gunning show that the method could easily be extended to the measurement of other isotopes of mercury. The extension and adaption of this technique to a study of the natural fractionation of mercury in ore deposits has not to our knowledge, been attempted. The technique warrants further study for possible geologic application.

NOBLE GASES

Until the work of Goleb (1966b), no analytical studies by atomic absorption had been reported for any of the noble gases. He reported a study of the atomic absorption of He, Ne, Ar, Kr, and Xe in the 3,000–8,500 Å range. A water-cooled hollow cathode discharge tube was used as an emission source. In Goleb's technique, the atoms are sputtered into the absorbing path in the hollow cathode discharge tube. Using this method, excitations to higher energy levels are accomplished more easily than with conventional flame absorption techniques.

The Schüller–Gollnow emission tube was operated at 30 mÅ, with a gas pressure of 2 mm Hg for each of noble gases studied. Emitted light was modulated by a 60 cycle mechanical chopper and focussed on the hole of a copper cylindrical insert that was the cathode electrode of the absorption tube. The absorption tube was operated at 75 mÅ using the noble gases at the following gas pressures: He 1.0, Ne 0.8, Ar 0.5, Kr 0.5, and Xe 0.5 mm of Hg.

Of the some 300 spectral lines checked, about one-third showed significant absorption, the highest values being 73.5% for the 6,402.25 line Ne and 73.7% for the 8,115.31 line of Ar. Approximately 6% of the lines tested absorbed more than 40%. Tables XXXIII–XXXVII list the results for the lines showing significant

TABLE XXXIII

ATOMIC ABSORPTION SPECTRUM OF HELIUM[1]

Wavelength[2] *(Å)*	*Intensity*[2]	*Percent absorption*
6,678.15	100	28.4
5,875.62	1,000	45.5
5,015.68	100	17.6
3,964.73	50	17.7
3,888.65	1,000	51.5
3,187.74	200	21.1

[1] Only absorptions greater than 10% are indicated. Modified after Goleb (1966a); reproduced by permission from *Anal. Chem.*
[2] Wavelength and intensities from ZAIDEL et al. (1961).

TABLE XXXIV

ATOMIC ABSORPTION SPECTRUM OF NEON[1]

Wavelength[2] *(Å)*	*Intensity*[2]	*Percent absorption*
8,377.61	800	11.2
7,245.16	1,000	15.3
7,032.41	1,000	34.7
6,929.47	1,000	26.1
6,678.28	500	25.0
6,598.95	100	18.2
6,402.25	2,000	73.5
6,382.99	1,000	45.4
6,334.42	1,000	38.5
6,266.49	1,000	35.5
6,217.28	1,000	13.3
6,163.59	1,000	24.2
6,143.06	1,000	52.3
6,096.16	300	38.0
6,074.33	1,000	26.7
5,944.83	500	33.3
5,881.89	1,000	23.0
5,852.48	2,000	18.9

[1] Only absorptions greater than 10% are indicated. Modified from GOLEB (1966a); reproduced by permission from *Anal. Chem.*
[2] Wavelength and intensities from ZAIDEL et al. (1961).

TABLE XXXV

ATOMIC ABSORPTION SPECTRUM OF ARGON[1]

Wavelength[2] *(Å)*	*Intensity*[2]	*Percent absorption*
8,424.65	2,000	51.1
8,115.31	5,000	73.7
8,014.79	800	59.1
8,006.16	600	31.6
7,948.18	400	38.7
7,635.11	500	72.6
7,514.65	200	53.1
7,503.87	700	28.5
7,383.98	400	48.3
7,067.22	400	30.6
6,965.43	400	34.8
5,373.49	500	16.6
5,221.27	500	15.8
5,054.18	300	23.5
5,048.81	500	31.6
3,675.22	300	11.8
3,670.64	300	11.8

[1] Only absorptions greater than 10% are indicated. Modified from GOLEB (1966a); reproduced by permission from *Anal. Chem.*
[2] Wavelength and intensities from ZAIDEL et al. (1961).

TABLE XXXVI

ATOMIC ABSORPTION SPECTRUM OF KRYPTON[1]

Wavelength[2] *(Å)*	*Intensity*[2]	*Percent absorption*
8,190.05	3,000	55.5
8,104.36	5,000	43.7
8,059.50	1,000	60.0
7,854.82	800	17.9
7,694.54	1,000	37.7
7,685.24	1,000	11.5
7,601.54	5,000	52.6
7,587.41	1,000	48.9
7,224.10	100	31.5

[1] Only absorptions greater than 10% are indicated. Modified from GOLEB (1966a); reproduced by permission from *Anal. Chem.*
[2] Wavelength and intensities from ZAIDEL et al. (1961).

TABLE XXXVII

ATOMIC ABSORPTION SPECTRUM OF XENON[1]

Wavelength[2] *(Å)*	*Intensity*[2]	*Percent absorption*
8,409.19	2,000	10.9
8,280.12	5,000	47.1
8,231.63	5,000	51.1
7,967.34	500	10.5
7,386.00	100	16.6
6,498.72	100	18.3
6,198.26	100	10.5
4,671.23	2,000	11.5

[1] Only absorptions greater than 10% are indicated. Modified after GOLEB (1966a); reproduced by permission from *Anal. Chem.*
[2] Wavelength and intensities from ZAIDEL et al. (1961).

absorption. Precision of the technique was tested using the 7,601.54 Kr line. The standard deviation from the mean in percent was ± 1.7. It should be emphasized that until further work is reported in the literature the absorption values given in the table apply only to the particular experimental conditions used in Goleb's laboratory. No data have been reported on studies of different gas mixtures, limits of detection or sensitivities.

Although to the author's knowledge, no study of the noble gases in geological samples has been done by atomic absorption, the implications and possibilities of this method warrant including it here.

References

AGAZZI, E. J., 1965. Determination of tin in hydrogen peroxide solutions by atomic absorption spectrometry. *Anal. Chem.*, 37: 364–366.

ALLAN, J. E., 1959. The determination of iron and manganese by atomic absorption. *Spectrochim. Acta*, 10: 800–806.

ALLAN, J. E., 1961a. Report of Third Australian Spectroscopy Conference, reviewed by R. A. Durie. *Nature*, 192: 927–929.

ALLAN, J. E., 1961b. The determination of zinc in agricultural materials by atomic absorption spectrophotometry. *Analyst*, 86: 530–534.

ALLAN, J. E., 1962. Atomic absorption spectrophotometry absorption lines and detection limits in the air-acetylene flame. *Spectrochim. Acta*, 18: 259–263.

ANDREW, T. R. and NICHOLS, P. N. R., 1962. The application of atomic absorption to the rapid determination of magnesium in electronic nickel and nickel alloys. *Analyst*, 87: 25–30.

ANGINO, E. E., 1965. Chemical analyses of recent sediments from Vieques Passage, Eastern Puerto Rico. *Texas A & M Res. Found., Proj. 417, Rept.*, 65–30 F: 73 pp.

ANGINO, E. E., 1967. Distribution of iron in the various components of Recent carbonate sediments. *Bull. Kansas Geol. Surv.*, 187(1): 3–5.

ANGINO, E. E. and BILLINGS, G. K., 1966. Lithium content of sea water by atomic absorption spectrometry. *Geochim. Cosmochim. Acta*, 30: 153–158.

ANGINO, E. E., BILLINGS, G. K. and ANDERSON, N., 1966. Observed variations in the strontium concentration of sea water. *Chem. Geol.*, 1: 145–153.

ANTWEILER, J. C. and LOVE, J. D., 1967. Gold-bearing sedimentary rocks in northwest Wyoming—a preliminary report. *U.S., Geol. Surv., Circ.*, 541: 12 pp.

BAKER, C. A. and GARTON, F. W. J., 1961. A study of interferences in emission and absorption flame photography. *U.K. At. Energy Authority Rept., AERA-R* 3490: 21 pp.

BARNES JR., L., 1966. Determination of chromium in low alloy steels by atomic absorption spectrometry. *Anal. Chem.*, 38: 1083–1085.

BARRAS, R. C., 1962. Application of atomic absorption to the petroleum industry. Jarrell–Ash Newsletter, 13 (June): 1–4.

BELCHER, C. B., 1963. The determination of iron in tungsten carbide by atomic absorption. *Anal. Chim. Acta*, 29: 340–343.

BELCHER, C. B. and BRAY, H. M., 1961. Determination of magnesium in iron by atomic absorption spectrophotometry. *Anal. Chim. Acta*, 26: 322–325.

BELCHER, C. B. and BROOKS, K. A., 1963. The determination of strontium in coal ash by atomic absorption spectrophotometry. *Anal. Chim. Acta*, 29: 202–205.

BELCHER, C. B. and KINSON, K., 1964. The determination of manganese in iron and steel by atomic absorption spectrophotometry. *Anal. Chim. Acta*, 30: 383–387.

BELCHER, R., DAGNALL, R. M. and WEST, T. S., 1964. An examination of the atomic absorption spectroscopy of silver. *Talanta*, 11: 1257–1263.

BELT JR., C. B., 1964. Atomic absorption spectrophotometry and the analysis of silicate rocks for copper and zinc. *Econ. Geol.*, 59: 240–258.

BILLINGS, G. K., 1963. *Major and Trace Element Relationships within Co-existing Minerals of the Enchanted Rock Batholith, Llano Uplift, Texas.* Thesis, Rice University, Houston, Texas, unpublished, 74 pp.

BILLINGS, G. K., 1965a. Light scattering in trace element analysis by atomic absorption. *At. Absorption Newsletter, Perkin–Elmer Corp.*, 4: 357–361.

BILLINGS, G. K., 1965b. The determination of potassium in oil field brines by atomic absorption spectrometry. *Bull. Can. Petrol. Geologists*, 13: 532–534.

BILLINGS, G. K., 1965c. The analysis of geological materials by atomic absorption spectrometry, 2. Accuracy tests. *At. Absorption Newsletter, Perkin–Elmer Corp.*, 4: 312–316.

BILLINGS, G. K. and ADAMS, J. A. S., 1964. The analysis of geological materials by atomic absorption spectrometry. *At. Absorption Newsletter, Perkin–Elmer Corp.*, 23: 1–7.

BILLINGS, G. K. and ANGINO, E. E., 1965. The determination of strontium in oil field brines by atomic absorption spectrometry. *Bull. Can. Petrol. Geologists*, 13: 529–531.

BILLINGS, G. K. and HARRISS, R. C., 1965. Cation analysis of marine waters by atomic absorption spectrometry: Gulf of Mexico coastal waters. *Texas J. Sci.*, 17: 129–138.

BOLING, E. A., 1965. An integrating analog computer for atomic absorption spectrometry. *Anal. Chem.*, 37: 482–485.

BOLING, E. A. 1966. A multiple slit burner for atomic absorption spectroscopy. *Spectrochim. Acta*, 22: 425–431.

BRECH, F., 1965. Improved technology in atomic absorption including multichannel approaches. *Jarrell–Ash Bull.*, July: 1–15.

BURRELL, D. C., 1965a. The determination of nickel and cobalt in natural waters by atomic absorption spectrophotometry: A preliminary study. *At. Absorption Newsletter, Perkin–Elmer Corp.*, 4: 309–311.

BURRELL, D. C., 1965b. The geochemistry and origin of amphibolites from Bamble, South Norway. *Norsk Geol. Tidsskr.*, 45: 21–30.

BURRELL, D. C., 1965c. An atomic absorption method for the determination of cobalt, iron, and nickel in the asphaltic fractions of Recent sediments. *At. Absorption Newsletter, Perkin–Elmer Corp.*, 4: 328–329.

BURROWS, J. A., HEERDT, J. C. and WILLIS, J. B., 1965. Determination of wear metals in used lubricating oils by atomic absorption spectrometry. *Anal. Chem.*, 37: 579–582.

BUTLER, L. R. P., 1962. A plastic burner for atomic absorption analysis of highly corrosive solutions. *J. S. African Inst. Mining Met.*, 62: 786–789.

BUTLER, L. R. P. and BRINK, D., 1963. The determination of magnesium, calcium, potassium, sodium, copper and iron in water samples by atomic absorption spectroscopy. *S. African Ind. Chemist*, 17: 152–156.

BUTLER, L. R. P. and MATTHEWS, P. M., 1966. The determination of trace quantities of molybdenum by atomic absorption spectroscopy. *Anal. Chim. Acta*, 36: 319–329.

BUTLER, L. R. P. and STRASHEIM, A., 1965. Multiple element atomic absorption analysis. *Spectrochim. Acta*, 21: 1207–1216.

CAPACHO-DELGADO, L. and MANNING, D. C., 1965. Determination of tin by atomic absorption. *At. Absorption Newsletter, Perkin–Elmer Corp.*, 4: 317–318.

CAPACHO-DELGADO, L. and MANNING, D. C., 1966. Determination of vanadium in steels and gas oils. *At. Absorption Newsletter, Perkin–Elmer Corp.*, 5: 1–3.

CAPACHO-DELGADO, L. and SPRAGUE, S., 1965. Calcium interference in atomic absorption analysis for barium. *At. Absorption Newsletter, Perkin–Elmer Corp.*, 4: 363–364.

CARTWRIGHT, J. S., SEBEN, C. and SLAVIN, W., 1966. Nickel high-brightness lamps. *At. Absorption Newsletter, Perkin–Elmer Corp.*, 5: 22–27.

CHAKRABARTI, C. L., LYLES, G. R. and DOWLING, F. B., 1963. The determination of aluminum by atomic absorption spectroscopy. *Anal. Chim. Acta*, 29: 489–499.

DAGNALL, R. M. and WEST, T. S., 1964. Observation on the atomic absorption spectroscopy of lead in aqueous solution, in organic extracts, and in gasoline. *Talanta*, 11: 1553–1557.

DAVID, D. J., 1958. Determination of zinc and other elements in plants by atomic absorption spectroscopy. *Analyst*, 83: 655–661.

DAVID, D. J., 1959. Determination of calcium in plant material by atomic absorption spectrophotometry. *Analyst*, 84: 536–545.

DAVID, D. J., 1960. The determination of exchangeable sodium, potassium, calcium, and magnesium in soils by atomic absorption spectrophotometry. *Analyst*, 85: 495–503.

DAVID, D. J., 1961. The determination of molybdenum by atomic absorption spectrophotometry. *Analyst*, 86: 730–740.

DAVID, D. J., 1962. Determination of strontium in biological materials and exchangeable strontium in soils by atomic absorption spectrophotometry. *Analyst*, 87: 576–585.

DEAN, J. A., 1960. *Flame Photometry*. McGraw-Hill, New York, N.Y., 354 pp.

DELAUGHTER, B., 1965. The determination of sub-ppm concentrations of chromium and molybdenum in brines. *At. Absorption Newsletter, Perkin–Elmer Corp.*, 4: 273–275.

DICKSON, R. E. and JOHNSON, C. M., 1966. Interferences associated with the determination of calcium by atomic absorption. *Appl. Spectry.*, 20: 214–218.

ELWELL, W. T. and GIDLEY, J. A. F., 1962. *Atomic Absorption Spectrophotometry*. Macmillan, New York, N.Y., 102 pp.
ERDEY, L., SVEHLA, G. and KOLTAI, L., 1963. The accuracy of zinc determination by atomic absorption methods. *Talanta*, 10: 531–536.

FABRICAND, B. P., IMBIMBO, E. S., BREY, M. E. and WESTON, J. A., 1966. Atomic absorption analyses for Li, Mg, K, Rb, and Sr in ocean waters. *J. Geophys. Res.*, 71: 3917–3922.
FABRICAND, B. P., SAWYER, R. R., UNGAR, S. G. and ADLER, S., 1962. Trace metal concentrations in the ocean by atomic absorption spectroscopy. *Geochim. Cosmochim. Acta*, 26: 1023–1027.
FARRAR, B., 1965. Determination of copper and zinc in ore samples and lead base alloys. *At. Absorption Newsletter, Perkin–Elmer Corp.*, 4: 325–327.
FARRAR, B., 1966. Determination of cadmium in ore and magnesium in rock samples. *At. Absorption Newsletter, Perkin–Elmer Corp.*, 5: 62.
FASSEL, V. A. and MOSSOTTI, V. G., 1963. Atomic absorption spectra of vanadium, titanium, niobium, scandium, yttrium, and rhenium. *Anal. Chem.*, 35: 252–253.
FASSEL, V. A., MOSSOTTI, V. G., GROSSMAN, W. E. L. and KNISELY, R. N., 1966. Evaluation of spectral continua as primary sources in atomic absorption spectroscopy. *Spectrochim. Acta*, 22: 347–357.
FISHMAN, M. J. and DOWNS, S. C., 1966. Methods for analysis of selected metals in water by atomic absorption. *U.S., Geol. Surv., Water Supply Paper*, 1540–C: 45 pp.
FIXMAN, M. and BOUGHTON, L., 1966. Mineral assay for silver, zinc, and cadmium by atomic absorption. *At. Absorption Newsletter, Perkin–Elmer Corp.*, 5: 33.
FLEISCHER, M. and STEVENS, R. E., 1962. Summary of new data on rock samples G-1 and W-1. *Geochim. Cosmochim. Acta*, 26: 525–543.
FUWA, K., PULIDO, P., MCKAY, R. and VALLEE, B. L., 1964. Determination of zinc in biological materials by atomic absorption spectrophotometry. *Anal. Chem.*, 36: 2407–2411.

GALLE, O. K. and ANGINO, E. E., 1967. The determination of calcium and magnesium in carbonate and silicate rocks by atomic absorption. *Bull. Kans. Geol. Surv.*, 185(1): 9–11.
GATEHOUSE, B. M. and WALSH, A., 1960. Analysis of metallic samples by atomic absorption spectroscopy. *Spectrochim. Acta*, 16: 602–604.
GILBERT JR., P. T. and ULRICH, W. F., 1965. *Notes on the Theory, Technique, and Application of Flame spectroscopy*. Beckman Instruments, Inc., Fullerton, Calif., 16 pp.
GOLEB, J. A., 1963. Uranium isotope investigations by atomic absorption. *Anal. Chem.*, 35: 1978.
GOLEB, J. A., 1966a. Near ultraviolet-visible atomic absorption spectra of the noble gases. *Anal. Chem.*, 38: 1059–1061.

GOLEB, J. A., 1966b. The application of hollow-cathode discharge tubes to spectrographic analysis. In: L. FOWLER, D. K. ROE and R. G. HARMON (Editors), *Analysis Instrumentation.* Plenum, New York, N.Y., pp. 229–238.

GOLEB, J. A., 1966c. The determination of uranium isotopes by atomic absorption spectrophotometry. *Anal. Chim. Acta*, 34: 135–145.

GOLEB, J. A., 1966d. An attempt to determine the boron natural abundance ratio, B^{11}/B^{10}, by atomic absorption spectrophotometry. *Anal. Chim. Acta*, in press.

GOLEB, J. A. and BRODY, J. K., 1963. Atomic absorption studies using a hollow-cathode tube as an absorption source. *Anal. Chim. Acta*, 28: 457–466.

GOLEB, J. A. and YOKOYAMA, Y., 1964. The use of a discharge tube as an absorption source for the determination of lithium-6 and lithium-7 isotopes by atomic absorption spectrophotometry. *Anal. Chim. Acta*, 30: 213–222.

GREAVES, M. C., 1963. Determination of gold and silver in solution by atomic absorption spectroscopy. *Nature*, 199: 552.

HARRISS, R. C., 1964. *The Transfer of Strontium, Iron, and Magnesium from Sea Water to Skeletal Carbonate Material.* Thesis, Rice University, Houston, Texas, unpublished, 51 pp.

HARRISS, R. C. and ALMY JR., C. C., 1964. A preliminary investigation into the incorporation and distribution of minor elements in the skeletal material of scleractinean corals. *Bull. Marine Sci. Gulf Caribbean*, 14: 418–423.

HARVEY, H. W., 1960. *The Chemistry and Fertility of Sea Waters.* Cambridge Univ. Press, London, 240 pp.

HELL, A., RAMIREZ-MUNOZ, J. and SHIFRIN, N., 1965. New atomic absorption accessory for U. V. visible spectrophotometers. *Anal. Chem. Appl. Spectr., 16th., Pittsburgh.*

HUFFMAN, C., MENSIK, J. D. and RADER, L. F., 1966. Determination of silver in mineralized rocks by atomic absorption spectrophotometry. *U.S., Geol. Surv., Profess. Papers*, 550-B: B 189–B 191.

INGAMELLS, C. O., 1966. Absorptiometric methods in rapid silicate analysis. *Anal. Chim.*, 38: 1228–1234.

JACKSON, M. L., 1958. *Soil Chemical Analysis.* Prentice-Hall, Englewood Cliffs, N. J., 498 pp.

JAWOROWSKI, R. J. and WEBERLING, R. P., 1966. Spectral interference. *At. Absorption Newsletter, Perkin–Elmer Corp.*, 5: 125–126.

JONES, A. H., 1965. Analysis of glass and ceramic frit by atomic absorption spectrophotometry. *Anal. Chem.*, 37: 1761–1762.

JOYNER, T. and FINLEY, J. S., 1966. The determination of manganese and iron in sea water by atomic absorption spectrometry. *At. Absorption Newsletter, Perkin–Elmer Corp.*, 5: 4–7.

KAHN, H. L., 1966. Instrumentation for atomic absorption. *J. Chem. Educ.*, 43 (1 and 2): A103.

KERBER, J. D., 1966. Direct determination of nickel in catalytic-cracking feedstocks by atomic absorption spectrophotometry. *Appl. Spectry.*, 20: 212–213.

KINSON, K., 1964. The determination of nickel in iron and steel by atomic absorption spectrophotometry. *Anal. Chim. Acta*, 30: 64–67.

KINSON, K. and BELCHER, C. B., 1964. The determination of minor amounts of copper in iron and steel by atomic absorption. *Anal. Chim. Acta*, 31: 180–183.

KINSON, K., HODGES, R. J. and BELCHER, C. B., 1963. The determination of chromium in low-alloy irons and steel by atomic absorption. *Anal. Chim. Acta*, 29: 134–138.

KNISELY, R. N., D'SILVA, A. P. and FASSEL, V. A., 1963. A sensitive premixed oxyacetylene atomizer-burner for flame emission and absorption spectrometry. *Anal. Chem.*, 35: 910–911.

KOIRTYOHANN, S. R. and FELDMAN, C., 1964. Atomic absorption spectroscopy using long absorption path lengths and a demountable hollow cathode lamp. In: J. E. FORRETTE and E. LANTERMAN (Editors), *Developments in Applied Spectroscopy*, Plenum, New York, N.Y., 3: 180–189.

KOIRTYOHANN, S. R. and PICKETT, E. E., 1965a. Spectral interferences in atomic absorption spectroscopy. *Soc. Appl. Spectry., 4th. Natl. Meeting, Denver, Colo.*

KOIRTYOHANN, S. R. and PICKETT, E. E., 1965b. Background corrections in long path atomic absorption spectrometry. *Anal. Chem.*, 37: 601–603.

KOIRTYOHANN, S. R. and PICKETT, E. E., 1966a. Spectral interferences in atomic absorption spectrometry. *Anal. Chem.*, 38: 585–587.

KOIRTYOHANN, S. R. and PICKETT, E. E., 1966b. Light scattering by particles in atomic absorption spectrometry. *Anal. Chem.*, 38: 1087–1088.

KOLTHOFF, I. M. and SANDELL, E. B., 1952. *Textbook of Quantitative Inorganic Analysis*, 3rd ed. Macmillan, New York, N.Y., 759 pp.

LAKANEN, E., 1962. On the analysis of soluble trace elements. *Ann. Agr. Fenniae*, 1: 109–117.

LOCKYER, R. and HAMES, G. E., 1959. The quantitative determination of some noble metals by atomic absorption spectroscopy. *Analyst*, 84: 385–387.

LOCKYER, R., SCOTT, R. E. and SLADE, S., 1961. Enhancement of atomic absorption in the flame by organic solvents. *Nature*, 189: 830–831.

LOVERING, T. G., LAKIN, H. W. and MCCARTHY, J. H., 1966. Tellurium and mercury in jasperoid samples. *U.S., Geol. Surv., Profess. Papers*, 550-B: B 138–B 141.

L'VOV, B. V., 1961. The analytical use of atomic absorption spectra. *Spectrochim. Acta*, 17: 761–770.

MAGEE, R. J. and RAHMAN, A. K. M., 1965. Determination of copper in sea water by atomic absorption spectroscopy. *Talanta*, 12: 409–416.

MANNING, D. C., 1964. The determination of aluminum by atomic absorption spectroscopy. *At. Absorption Newsletter, Perkin-Elmer Corp.*, 24: 6–10.

MANNING, D. C., 1965. A burner for nitrous-oxide acetylene flames. *At. Absorption Newsletter, Perkin–Elmer Corp.*, 4: 267–271.

MANNING, D. C., 1966. The nitrous oxide–acetylene flame in atomic absorption spectroscopy. *At. Absorption Newsletter, Perkin–Elmer Corp.*, 5: 127–134.

MANNING, D. C. and SLAVIN, W., 1962. Lithium isotope analysis by atomic absorption spectrophotometry. *At. Absorption Newsletter, Perkin–Elmer Corp.*, 8: 1–5.

MANNING, D. C. and SLAVIN, W., 1964. Determination of selenium and tellurium in copper in atomic absorption spectrophotometry. *At. Absorption Newsletter, Perkin–Elmer Corp.*, 20: 1–9.

MANNING, D. C., SPRAGUE, S. and SLAVIN, W., 1963. The determination of aluminum by atomic absorption spectrophotometry. *Conf. Anal. Chem. Appl. Spectry., Pittsburgh.*

MANNING, D. C., TRENT, D. and VOLLMER, J., 1965. Dual-element magnesium–calcium hollow cathode lamp. *At. Absorption Newsletter, Perkin–Elmer Corp.*, 4: 234–236.

MANSELL, R. E. and EMMEL, H. W., 1965. Trace element extractions from brine with APDC and oxine. *At. Absorption Newsletter, Perkin–Elmer Corp.*, 4: 365–366.

MCNALLY JR., J. R., HARRISON, G. R. and ROWE, E., 1947. A hollow-cathode source applicable to spectrographic analysis for the halogens and gases. *J. Opt. Soc.* Am., 37: 93–98.

MCPHERSON, G. L., 1963. Some applications of atomic absorption spectroscopy in the determination of metals in alloys, paints, and plastics. *Australian Acad. Sci., 4th Aust. Spec. Conf.*, October, pp.1–3.

MCPHERSON, G. L., PRICE, J. W. and SCAIFE, P. H., 1963. Application of atomic absorption spectroscopy to the determination of cobalt in steel, alloy steel, and nickel. *Nature*, 199: 371–372.

MEANS, E. A. and RATCLIFF, D., 1965. Determination of wear metals in lubricating oils by atomic absorption spectroscopy. *At. Absorption Newsletter, Perkin–Elmer Corp.*, 4: 174–179.

MENZIES, A. C., 1960. A study of atomic absorption spectroscopy. *Anal. Chem.*, 32: 898–904.

MITCHELL, A. C. G. and ZEMANSKY, M. W., 1934. *Resonance Radiation and Excited Atoms.* Cambridge Univ. Press, London, 338 pp.

MOSSOTTI, V. G. and FASSEL, V. A., 1964. The atomic absorption spectra of the lanthanide elements. *Spectrochim. Acta*, 20: 1117–1127.

MOSTYN, R. A., 1967. Determination of antimony by atomic absorption spectrometry. *Anal. Chem.*, 39: 433–435.

MOSTYN, R. A. and CUNNINGHAM, A. F., 1966. Determination of molybdenum in ferrous alloys by atomic absorption spectrometry. *Anal. Chem.*, 38: 121–123.

MULFORD, C. E., 1966. Gallium and indium determinations by atomic absorptions. *At. Absorption Newsletter, Perkin–Elmer Corp.*, 5: 28–30.

NAKAGAWA, H. M. and LAKIN, H. W., 1965. A field method for the determination of silver in soils and rocks. *U.S., Geol. Surv., Profess. Papers*, 525-C: C 172–C 175.

NELSON, L. S. and KUEBLER, N. A., 1963. Vaporization of elements for atomic absorption spectroscopy with capacitor discharge lamps. *Spectrochim. Acta*, 19: 781–784.

OBERMILLER, E. L. and FREEDMAN, R. W., 1965. Rapid determination of calcium, magnesium, sodium, potassium, and iron in coal ash by atomic absorption spectrophotometry. *Fuel*, 44: 199–203.

OLSEN, A. M., 1965. Gold assay by atomic absorption spectrophotometry: A preliminary report. *At. Absorption Newsletter, Perkin–Elmer Corp.*, 4: 278–280.

OSBORN, K. R. and GUNNING, H. E., 1955. Determination of Hg^{202} and other mercury isotopes in samples of mercury vapor by mercury resonance radiation absorbiometry. *J. Opt. Soc. Am.*, 45: 552–555.

PERKINS, J., 1963. The determination of sodium in halo-phosphate phosphors by atomic absorption spectroscopy. *Analyst*, 88: 324–326.

PERRAULT, G., 1966. Spectrophotometric d'absorption atomique: une mise en garde sur la preparation des etalons de comparaisons. *Can. Spectry.*, 11: 19–20.

PLATTE, J. A. and MARCY, V. M., 1965. Atomic absorption spectrophotometry as a tool for the water chemist. *At. Absorption Newsletter, Perkin–Elmer Corp.*, 4: 289–292.

PRICE, V. and RAGLAND, P. C., 1966a. Trace metals in quartz by atomic absorption spectrophotometry. *Southeastern Geol.*, 7: 93–100.

PRICE, V. and RAGLAND, P. C., 1966b. A preliminary evaluation of the chemical character of ground water in a part of the Piedmont Province of North Carolina. *Univ. N. Carolina Water Resources Paper*, 18: 8 pp.

PULIDO, P., FUWA, K. and VALLEE, B. L., 1966. Determination of cadmium in biological materials by atomic absorption spectrophotometry. *Anal. Biochem.*, 14: 393–404.

RAGLAND, P. C. and BILLINGS, G. K., 1965. Composition of minerals within the wall rocks of a granitic batholith. *Southeastern Geol.*, 6: 87–115.

RAMAKRISHNA, T. V., ROBINSON, J. W. and WEST, P. W., 1957. Determination of copper, cadmium, and zinc by atomic absorption spectroscopy. *Anal. Chim. Acta*, 37: 20–26.

RANN, C. S. and HAMBLY, A. N., 1965. Distribution of atoms in an atomic absorption flame. *Anal. Chem.*, 37: 879–884.

RAWLING, B. S., AMOS, M. D. and GREAVES, M. C., 1961. The determination of silver in lead sulphide concentrate by atomic absorption spectroscopy. *Australasian Inst. Mining Met. Proc.*, 119: 1–17.

ROBINSON, J. W., 1960. Determination of sodium by atomic absorption spectroscopy. *Anal. Chim. Acta*, 23: 458–461.

ROBINSON, J. W., 1961a. Determination of lead in gasoline by atomic absorption spectroscopy. *Anal. Chim. Acta*, 24: 451–455.

ROBINSON, J. W. 1961b. Recent advances in atomic absorption spectroscopy. *Anal. Chem.*, 33: 1067–1071.

ROSSELAND, S., 1936. *Theoretical Astrophysics*. Clarendon Press, Oxford, 335 pp.

RUBESKA, I. and MOLDAN, B., 1965. Determination of magnesium in silicate and carbonate rocks by atomic absorption spectrophotometry. *Acta. Chim. Acad. Sci. Hung.*, 44: 367–371.

RUBESKA, I. and SVOBODA, V., 1964. Some causes of bending of analytical curves in atomic absorption spectroscopy. *Anal. Chim. Acta,* 32: 253–261.

RUBESKA, I., MOLDAN, B. and VALNIY, Z., 1963. The determination of sodium in pure limestones by atomic absorption spectrophotometry. *Anal. Chim. Acta,* 29: 206–210.

RUBESKA, I., SULCEK, Z. and MOLDAN, B., 1967. The determination of silver in sulfide minerals by atomic absorption spectrophotometry. *Anal. Chim. Acta,* 37: 27–32.

SACHDEV, S. L., ROBINSON, J. W. and WEST, P. W., 1967. Determination of vanadium by atomic absorption spectrophotometry. *Anal. Chim. Acta,* 37: 12–19.

SCOTT, R., 1966. Origin of chemical variations within ignimbrite cooling units. *Am. J. Sci.*, 264: 273–288.

SEBENS, C., VOLLMER, J. and SLAVIN, W., 1964. Multi-element hollow cathode lamps. *At. Absorption Newsletter, Perkin–Elmer Corp.*, 3: 165–169.

SIMMONS, E. C., 1965. Gold assay by atomic absorption spectrophotometry. *At. Absorption Newsletter, Perkin–Elmer Corp.*, 4: 281–287.

SLAVIN, W., 1964a. Atomic absorption instrumentation and technique—a review. In: L. FOWLER, D. K. LOE and R. G. HARMON (Editors), *Analysis Instrumentation.* Plenum, New York, N.Y., pp. 235–251.

SLAVIN, W., 1964b. Some data on ammonium pyrrolidine dithiocarbamate. *At. Absorption Newsletter, Perkin–Elmer Corp.*, 3: 141–143.

SLAVIN, W., 1965. The application of atomic absorption spectroscopy to geochemical prospecting and mining. *At. Absorption Newsletter, Perkin–Elmer Corp.*, 4: 243–254.

SLAVIN, W., 1966. Recent developments in analytical atomic absorption spectroscopy. *At. Absorption Newsletter, Perkin–Elmer Corp.*, 5: 42–45.

SLAVIN, W. and MANNING, D. C., 1963. Atomic absorption spectrophotometry in strongly reducing oxyacetylene flames. *Anal. Chem.*, 35: 253–254.

SLAVIN, W., TRENT, D. J. and SPRAGUE, S., 1965. The determination of rubidium by atomic absorption spectrophotometry. *At. Absorption Newsletter, Perkin–Elmer Corp.*, 4: 180–185.

SLAVIN, W., VENGHIATTIS, A. and MANNING, D. C., 1966. Some recent experience with the nitrous oxide-acetylene flame. *At. Absorption Newsletter, Perkin–Elmer Corp.*, 5: 84–88.

SPRAGUE, S., 1963. Cement analysis. *At. Absorption Newsletter, Perkin–Elmer Corp.*, 14: 9–14.

SPRAGUE, S. and SLAVIN, W., 1963. Determination of the metal content of lubricating oils by atomic absorption spectrophotometry. *At. Absorption Newsletter, Perkin–Elmer Corp.*, 12: 4–6.

SPRAGUE, S. and SLAVIN, W., 1964a. Determination of very small amounts of copper and lead in KCl by organic extraction and atomic absorption spectrophotometry. *At. Absorption Newsletter, Perkin–Elmer Corp.*, 20: 11–15.

SPRAGUE, S. and SLAVIN, W., 1964b. The determination of nickel in urine by atomic absorption spectrophotometry—preliminary study. *At. Absorption Newsletter, Perkin–Elmer Corp.*, 3: 160–164.

SPRAGUE, S. and SLAVIN, W., 1965. Performance of the three-slot Boling burner. *At. Absorption Newsletter, Perkin–Elmer Corp.*, 4: 293–295.

STRASHEIM, A. and WESSELS, G. J., 1963. The atomic absorption determination of some noble metals. *Appl. Spectry.*, 17: 65–70.

STRASHEIM, A., NORVAL, E. and BUTLER, L. R. P., 1964. The atomic absorption determination of traces of lead in fish flour. *J. S. African Chem. Inst.*, 17: 55–60.

STRASHEIM, A., STRELOW, F. W. E. and BUTLER, L. R. P., 1960. The determination of copper by means of atomic absorption spectroscopy. *J. S. African Chem. Inst.*, 13: 73–81.

SULLIVAN, J. V. and WALSH, A., 1965. High intensity hollow-cathode lamps. *Spectrochim. Acta*, 21: 721–726.

TINDALL, F. M., 1965. Silver and gold assay by atomic absorption spectrophotometry. *At. Absorption Newsletter, Perkin–Elmer Corp.*, 4: 399–400.

TINDALL, F. M., 1966. Notes on silver and gold assay by atomic absorption. *At. Absorption Newsletter, Perkin–Elmer Corp.*, 5: 140.

TOLANSKY, S., 1947. *High Resolution Spectroscopy*. Methuen, London, 291 pp.

TRENT, D. J. and SLAVIN, W., 1964a. The direct determination of trace quantities of nickel in catalytic cracking feedstocks by atomic absorption spectrophotometry. *At. Absorption Newsletter, Perkin–Elmer Corp.*, 3: 131–140.

TRENT, D. J. and SLAVIN, W., 1964b. Determination of the major metals in granitic and diabasic rocks by atomic absorption spectrophotometry. *At. Absorption Newsletter, Perkin–Elmer Corp.*, 19: 1–6.

TRENT, D. J. and SLAVIN, W., 1964c. Determination of various metals in silicate samples by atomic absorption spectrophotometry. *At. Absorption Newsletter, Perkin–Elmer Corp.*, 3: 118–125.

VAUGHN, W. W., 1967. A simple mercury vapor detector for geochemical prospecting. *U.S., Geol. Surv., Circ.*, 540: 8 pp.

VAUGHN, W. W. and MCCARTHY JR., J. H., 1964. An instrumental technique for the determination of submicrogram concentrations of mercury in soils, rocks, and gas. *U.S., Geol. Surv., Profess. Papers*, 501 D (2): D 123–D 127.

WALSH, A., 1955. The application of atomic absorption spectra to chemical analysis. *Spectrochim. Acta*, 7: 108–117.

WALSH, A., 1961. Application of atomic absorption spectra to chemical analysis. In: H. W. THOMPSON (Editor), *Advances in Spectroscopy*. Interscience, New York, N.Y., 11: 1–22.

WHEAT, J. A., 1964. Determination of metallic impurities in water by atomic absorption spectrometry. *Office Tech. Serv., U.S. Dept. Commerce, DP-879 (a report by Du Pont on contract AT (07-2-1))—AEC Res. Development Rept., TID-4500:* 15 pp.

WHEAT, J. A., 1965. Applications of atomic absorption spectroscopy. *Office of Technical Services, U.S. Dept. Commerce, DP–980 (a report by Du*

Pont on contract AT (07–2–1) AEC Research and Development Report, TID–4500: 20 pp.

WILLIS, J. B., 1960a. The determination of metals in blood serum by atomic absorption spectroscopy, 1. Calcium. *Spectrochim. Acta*, 16: 259–272.

WILLIS, J. B., 1960b. The determination of metals in blood serum by atomic absorption spectroscopy, 2. Magnesium *Spectrochim. Acta*, 16: 273–278.

WILLIS, J. B., 1960c. The determination of metals in blood serum by atomic absorption spectroscopy, 3. Sodium and potassium. *Spectrochim. Acta*, 16: 551–558.

WILLIS, J. B., 1961. Determination of calcium and magnesium in urine by atomic absorption spectroscopy. *Anal. Chem.*, 33: 556–559.

WILLIS, J. B., 1962. Determination of lead and other heavy metals in urine by atomic absorption spectroscopy. *Anal. Chem.*, 34: 614–617.

WILLIS, J. B., 1963. Analysis of biological materials by atomic absorption spectroscopy. In: D. GLICK (Editor), *Methods of Biochemical Analysis*, Interscience, New York, N.Y., XI: 1–67.

WILLIS, J. B., 1965. The nitrous oxide-acetylene flame in atomic absorption spectroscopy. *Nature*, 207: 715–716.

WILSON, L., 1963. The determination of the solubility of zinc oxide in various solutions by atomic absorption spectroscopy. *Australia, Dept. Supply, Rept.*, ARL/MET 17: 17 pp.

WILSON, L., 1964a. A composite scheme for the analysis of aluminum alloys by atomic absorption spectroscopy. *Australia, Dept. Supply, Rept.*, ARL/MET 52: 14 pp.

WILSON, L., 1964b. The determination of silver in aluminum alloys by atomic absorption spectroscopy. *Anal. Chim. Acta*, 30: 377–383.

WILSON, L., 1965. The determination of cadmium in stainless steel by atomic absorption spectroscopy. *Australia, Dept. Supply, Tech. Memo*, ARL/MET 244: 10 pp.

ZAIDEL, A. N. and KORENNOI, E. P., 1961. Spectral determination of the isotope composition and concentration of lithium in solutions. *Opt. Spectry. (U.S.S.R.) (English Transl.)*, 10: 299–302.

ZAIDEL, A. N., PROKOFJEW, W. K. and RAISKI, S. M., 1961. *Tables of Spectrum Lines*. Verlag Technik, Berlin, 550 pp.

PART III

Appendix to the First Edition

APPENDIX TO CHAPTER 3

Recent Developments in Instrumentation

The last few years have seen an increase in both the number of manufacturers of atomic absorption equipment and in the development of various parts of the instrument that have improved analytical capability. We shall not attempt to list or describe all of the new instruments for sale, but they now number on the order of 15 to 20 different manufacturers.

Light sources still depend primarily on hollow cathode lamps. However, these have been continuously improved particularly from the standpoint of shielding with some type of insulating shield between cathode and anode. There have also been improvements in high intensity lamps using coated auxiliary electrodes. The coating is an electron emissive material. The electrodes are powered separately to give rise to an area of high electron density that interacts with the atomic vapor cloud. The ion lines are reduced in intensity, whereas the resonance lines are increased in intensity. Electrodeless discharge lamps using metal placed in a resonant cavity coupled to a radio frequency field are increasingly being used because of the intense, pure spectrum with extremely narrow lines. Such lamps are particularly used for As, In and Ga where high intensity is not available in the hollow cathode lamps.

Obviously, an improvement in a signal-to-noise ratio can be gained if the amount of sample reaching the flame in very small particles can be increased. Several processes are used, such as heated burner chambers (memory problems), impact beads in the nebulizer, counter-jet nebulizers, and ultrasonic nebulization. The counter-jet nebulizer seems to have the best characteristics. An increased use of this method can be expected.

The analysis of solutions containing a high percentage of dissolved solids has always been a problem in flame analytical methods. The Boling burner was developed by Perkin–Elmer and can handle samples with a maximum total solids of about 4–6%. A high solids burner has been designed for the Instrumentation Laboratory Atomic Absorption unit. The slit is 6 cm long by 0.05 inch. wide. The flame does not flash back into the chamber with the wide slot because the head of the burner is made of 15 mm-wide stainless steel which (by conduction) cools the slot. Samples for total solids up to 40% can be run without clogging.

Early use of atomic absorption (for refractory elements) was hindered by formation of oxides in the flame. This has been largely overcome by use of the nitrous oxide–acetylene flame. In addition, the higher temperature of these flames removes many residual chemical interferences. For example, magnesium is not affected by aluminum. Ionization interference, however, is increased by the high flame temperatures. The nitrous oxide–acetylene flame also is generally noisier.

As would be expected, there have been constant attempts to improve detection limits. Some of these methods have involved extraction techniques as discussed in other sections of the book. Other methods have involved introduction of the sample in the flame. Two of these show a high degree of promise for reaching very low detection limits. They do, however, increase the analytical time per sample. Both of these methods make use of increased atomization efficiency. One is a sample boat developed by Perkin–Elmer. A sample is placed in a small Ta boat. The boat is then placed beside the flame and the solvent evaporated. After the sample dries, the boat is placed directly over the flame using the flame heat to vaporize the entire sample into the optical path. Improvements in detection limits have been observed to range from 5 to 50x. Care must be taken to avoid interferences and to account for particle scatter. Varian Techtron has developed a carbon rod atomizer. In the atomizer, the atom population is produced just above the central section of the electrically heated rod from a sample deposited in the small cavity in the top of the rod. An inert gas shield is provided continuously, and the device requires water cooling. With the carbon rod atomizer, light scattering and molecular absorption are observed through the various cooling and recombination processes. When the inert gas atmosphere is replaced by a diffusion flame, condensation and recombination are prevented, and thus, the spectral interferences are greatly reduced. Although there are still problems regarding chemical interference, and although the atomizer is relatively expensive, it can be expected that increased use of such methods will be made because of increased sensitivity and simplicity of sample preparation.

Detailed information on new instrumental parameters and theoretical developments are presented in two excellent reference books (CHRISTIAN and FELDMAN, 1970; MAVRODINEANU, 1970).

APPENDIX TO CHAPTER 4

Interferences

Most of the general causes of interferences are discussed in the earlier edition of this book. One of those was molecular absorption, and there was a rather detailed method of correcting for this particular nonspecific absorption. The recognition of this interference has resulted in various types of background correction devices. Recently both Instrumentation Laboratories and Perkin–Elmer Corp. have introduced background correction systems. In the Perkin–Elmer 303, a deuterium arc is time shared along with the hollow cathode. The instrument operates as a single beam system when the correction system is used as the reference channel is blocked out. Both beams are passed through the flame, and a ratio is taken. The disadvantages of this are that an exact time of matching the two beams is difficult, residual background effects are evident, and the double beam feature of the instrument is eliminated.

The Instrumentation Laboratory system also uses a deuterium arc. The arc is placed in the second channel which is also double beam and a hollow cathode in the first channel. The nonspecific absorbance from the second channel is then automatically substracted from the line absorbance of the sample channel giving rise to an error free background correction. These correction systems are particularly useful to analysists working with geological samples because the molecular absorption interference is a serious one (BILLINGS and RAGLAND, 1969).

It was stated in the previous edition of this book that disagreement of interference effects as shown by various authors was probably the result of variation in flame characteristics and burner positions. The importance of flame characteristics such as gas ratios and the position of the burner relative to the optic system has been carefully delineated with respect to nitrous oxide–acetylene flames by MARX and WELCHER (1970). Their studies illustrated the complexity of cation interference effects, the magnitude, and in some cases the direction of interferences dependent upon a variety of experimental variables. The evaporation rate of small salt particles in the flame is a complex function of many factors, including drop size, diffusion coefficient of the evaporating species, surface tension, and heat-transfer characteristics. Many interferences can be reduced or eliminated by the proper selection of flame conditions and salt concentration. The effect of solute and burner characteristics has been further investigated by FASSEL and BECKER (1969) in which they consider the classical interference of phosphates on alkaline earths. They have clearly shown that the chemical interference of alkaline earth-phosphate, and alkaline earth-sulfate is a function of the solvent used and of the flame conditions. Such studies on general interferences as a function of flame characteristics clearly point out the need for careful standardization by every analyst of his system and the fact that he cannot depend in detail on interference tests run by someone else.

MANNING and CHABOT (1968) have studied a rather unusual effect that can seriously interfere with various atomic absorption analyses. Apparently, a number of acetylene tanks contain acetone vapor. The amount of acetone vapor in the acetylene does affect the absorption response of numerous elements. The amount of acetone reaching the flame is a function of tank pressure, and thus, tank pressure may cause a variation in the absorbance for various elements. The main danger here is that analyses will be made at different times than when standards were run and that this time difference has allowed a change in tank pressure, and thus, acetone vapor in the flame. This, of course, can be alleviated by running standards constantly with the analyses. The effects of this acetone vapor change will probably be significant for people using automated equipment unless they consistently run standards in their automated process. Interferences in the determination of specific elements are listed below.

SPECIFIC ELEMENT INTERFERENCES

Tin

The effect of organic solvent on tin species has been studied by HARRISON and JULIANO (1969). The presence of alcohols, ketones, and organic acids, even at low concentrations, has been shown to greatly reduce the atomic absorbance of Sn. Atomic absorbances of Ba and Mg are depressed in a manner similar to Sn while Zn and Cu absorbances are enhanced by the organic acids. The organics appeared to reduce the effective hydrogen atom population in the flame producing a drop in the Sn atomic population.

LEVINE et al. (1970) has shown that K enhances the absorption signal of Sn. This effect has also been shown for Na and NH_4^+. The effect is particularly noticeable in the nitrous oxide–acetylene flame. JULIANO and HARRISON (1970) have summarized many of the atomic absorption interferences in the analysis for Sn. The inorganic acid depressed Sn absorption while alkali and alkaline earth metals produced enhancements. Aluminum has a negative effect while Ti exhibits a positive effect. Among the transition metals investigated, Co and Cu produced enhancement while Zn had no effect. Comparative studies done in the air–acetylene and nitrogen–hydrogen entrained air flames show that although Sn has a greater sensitivity in the hydrogen flame, it is also much more subject to interferences than in the air–acetylene flame. The analysis for Sn shows interferences from HNO_3 and sometimes from H_2SO_4 and phosphoric acid, and a depression of absorption in the air–acetylene flame by high concentrations of SO_4^{2-} and phosphate (CHRISTIAN and FELDMAN, 1970).

Arsenic

Major interference in the atomic absorption determination of As results from molecular absorption (MENIS and RAINS, 1969). Many elements in concentrations greater than 1 mg/ml, produce an absorption at the As wave lengths. Corrections can be made by using the Ne 1916 Å or 1930 Å line, or a non-absorbing As line at 1990 Å. No interference of HCl or HNO_3 was observed up to 1 *N* acidity. An electrodeless discharge lamp was used as a source of radiation. CHRISTIAN and FELDMAN (1970) report that the sensitivity of As determination is enhanced by adding $CuSO_4$ or $Cu(NO_3)_2$ but is diminished by Cl^-. GUPTA et al. (1968) tested a large number of potentially interfering ions on the determination of Ga. The list of both interfering and non-interfering ions is too long to be reproduced here, and the reader is referred to their original paper. However, it should be pointed out that there were a number of interfering ions and that a solvent effect was also noticeable in that methanol, ethanol, and acetone (50% v/v) decreased the sensitivity while a 40% (v/v) solution of acetone and isobutyl alcohol had no effect.

Antimony

SLAVIN and SATTUR (1968) have reported on tests showing spectral interference during the determination of Sb by absorption due to Pb on a wavelength 0.24 Å away from the major antimony line. They suggest that if one wishes to determine Sb in the presence of significant amounts of Pb that the Sb resonance lines at 2068.33 Å and 2311.5 Å be used in order to avoid this spectral interference. CHRISTIAN and FELDMAN (1970) report that 1000 p.p.m. of 15 different metals does not interfere with the determination of Sb. However, Cu does cause a slight enhancement at certain wavelengths. HCl, HNO_3 and especially H_2SO_4 decrease absorption, and therefore, the pH of samples must be carefully controlled.

Zirconium

The absorption by Zr atoms in the nitrous oxide–acetylene flame is enhanced in the presence of many nitrogen containing compounds (BOND and WILLIS, 1968). Both HF and Fe enhance the sensitivity of Zr analysis. (CHRISTIAN and FELDMAN, 1970).

Silver

WEST et al. (1967) discussed the interference of various ions on the determination of Ag. Of a large number of ions tested, they found some negative interference by Au, reasonable high concentrations of silica, and surfactants.

Rubidium

CHRISTIAN and FELDMAN (1970) report on European data for interferences in the determination of Rb. They indicate that for 1 p.p.m. Rb in the presence of 1000 p.p.m. Na, Sr, Fe, Cu, Mn, Cr, Ba, Si, Ti, or Li and 500 p.p.m. Mg or Ca, no interference was found.

Beryllium

While many ions have been tested for interference with the determination of Be two materials which have been found to cause interference are Al and CH_3COOH (CHRISTIAN and FELDMAN, 1970).

Magnesium

Depressive interferences have been shown for Ti, Zr, Hf and Th in the determination of 6 p.p.m. Mg in the presence of 1000 p.p.m. of the interfering element. Many of these interferences are due to the formation of oxides and they can be decreased or negated by use of a nitrous oxide–acetylene flame.

Calcium

Many acids interfere with Ca analysis, such as HCl, HNO_3, H_3PO_4 and CCl_3COOH. The effect can be overcome by matching acid strength of the standards and samples. The determination of Ca in natural waters is highly pH-dependent, and this is probably due to presence of HCO_3^- which produces $CaCO_3$ in the flame. This interference can be overcome by the addition of La.

Yttrium

HNO_3 and Ce enhance the ionization of Y, whereas H_2SO_4, $HClO_4$, HNO_3 and phosphoric acids and F^-, Si and Al suppress the absorption.

Titanium

Ti absorption in a nitrous oxide–acetylene flame is enhanced by the presence of Fe. In the presence of 5000 p.p.m. Fe, the elements Cr, Co, Ni, Mn, Cu, Nb, W, Mo and Ta did not interfere with Ti (CHRISTIAN and FELDMAN, 1970). Aluminium may cause enhancement of the Ti signal.

Hafnium

Fe in the presence of F^- enhances absorption.

Vanadium

With an oxy-acetylene flame, ten-fold excess of Sb, Cu, W, Bi, Th, Mo, U, Sn, Ti, Fe and Zr do not cause interference. In a nitrous oxide–acetylene flame, enhancement occurs by interference due to Li, Na, K, Ce, Fe, Cr, Bi, Al, Ti and phosphoric acid. This interference may be decreased by adding excess Al to the solution (CHRISTIAN and FELDMAN, 1970).

Chromium

Iron markedly suppresses the absorption of Cr. This interference can be offset by use of Al or NH_4 Cl. Alkali and alkaline earth chlorides also are interference suppressors (BARNES, 1966).

Molybdenum

Large amounts of Fe suppress Mo absorption.

Manganese

In an air–acetylene flame, the only serious interference with Mn appears to be from Si which causes a decrease in absorption (SACHDEV et al., 1967). In an oxy-hydrogen flame a slight suppression by Ti, V and Zr occur.

Rhenium

In a fuel rich oxy-acetylene flame, Cu, Pb, K and Mo cause a slight suppression. Fe is intermediate, and Al, Mn and Ca cause severe suppression in the determination of Re.

Cobalt

A large number of elements have been investigated at levels up to 2,000 p.p.m. and no particular interference was found (SACHDEV et al., 1967).

Copper

The mineral acids H_2SO_4, HCl and $HClO_4$ cause a slight reduction in absorption, in an oxy-hydrogen flame, and in an oxy-acetylene flame. Using a cool flame, no interference from forty-fold excess of several cations has been found, although small deviations were found with hundred-fold excesses. Anions cause no marked effect at ten-fold excess (CHRISTIAN and FELDMAN, 1970).

Mercury

CN^-, I^- and $S_2O_3^{2-}$ interfere with Hg determination as does 1000 p.p.m. of As and 100 to 200 p.p.m. Se, Te, Cr and Mn. Some evidence has been presented to indicate interference by Te, Au, Pt and acetone (CHRISTIAN and FELDMAN, 1970).

Rare-earth elements

The most serious interference with Nd and Eu is caused by F^-, SiO_2 and Al.

Aluminum

AMOS and THOMAS (1965) report no interference from 20 g/l of Ca, Zn, Cu, Pb, Mg, Na_3PO_4 or Na_2SO_4 in a nitrogen–oxygen–acetylene flame. Similar results were obtained with a nitrous oxide–acetylene flame.

Indium

The interferences listed for Ga are similar to those found in the determination of In.

Thallium

Sodium, K, Ca, Ba, Sr, Pb, Cu, Ni, Mg, Zr, Cd, Hg, Mn, Ag, Fe, Al, Cr, SO_4^-, PO_4^{3-}, ClO_4^- and NO_3^- at the 100 p.p.m. level all enhance the Tl absorption. This interference can be reduced significantly in the presence of 5000 p.p.m. of Li, Na or K (CHRISTIAN and FELDMAN, 1970).

Bismuth

In an oxy-acetylene flame Zn, Sn, Sb, Pb, Ni, Hg, Cu, Cd, As and Ag do not cause interferences. The degree of flame interferences, such as an absorption by OH, is a function of fuel mixture and can also be reduced by use of organic solvents.

Tellurium

High concentrations of Cu, Na, Zn and Ca interfere with Te absorption (CHAKRABARTI, 1967a).

APPENDIX TO CHAPTER 5

Recent Developments in the Analysis of Water

In the period since 1967, water analysis for both major and trace constituents by atomic absorption has increased tremendously. This would be expected because of the inherent simplicity of using water samples during atomic absorption analysis and because of the sensitivity and precision of which atomic absorption is capable. This turn of events would be expected to increase even more drastically in the next few years because of the increased impetus on trace metal studies for environmental pollution problems.

In addition to water analyses, atomic absorption is also being used for analysis of air-borne pollutants and although no discussion of this aspect is presented in this appendix, the "References to the appendix" (p.177) contains references to air pollution analyses by atomic absorption.

No attempt is made here to completely cover all of the literature of various types of water analyses that have been done recently by atomic absorption spectrometry. The approach has been to list some of the applications that seem to have the broadest potential for being used by other analysts.

One of the major developments has been continued experimentation with organic extraction for the determination of trace metals. As would be expected, some of this application has been in the area of chemical analysis of sea water (BROOKS et al., 1967, 1968).

A brief description of the extraction method used is as follows: Samples (250 ml) of interstitial water were acidified with twice-distilled constant boiling hydrochlocric acid to reduce the pH to 4. To each sample was added 25 ml of methylisobutyl ketone (MIBK) and 5 ml of 1% ammonium pyrrolidine dithiocarbanate (APDC). The APDC was purified by equilibration with an equal volume of MIBK and rejection of the organic phase. The sample mixtures were equilibrated for 30 min. in a shaking rack, and the phases were removed by a separatory funnel. Standards consisted of 250 ml of previously extracted sea water samples containing incremental amounts of added ions. These were extracted in 20 ml quantities of MIBK after addition of APDC as before. The smaller volume of solvent made allowance for the solubility of MIBK in the unequilibrated original sample. With scale expansion of x10, limits of detection were below 0.2 p.p.b. for most elements, and the coefficients of variation for replicate analyses were in most cases below 10% except for Co (15%). The elements determined were Cd, Co, Cu, Fe, Ni and Zn.

The method of organic extraction has also been applied to concentrated brines by BILLINGS and RAGLAND (1969). Their procedure, which involved oil field brines and samples up to approximately 250,000 p.p.m. total solids, is as follows: The volume of brine is recorded and the pH adjusted to 2.5–3 with concentrated HCl. Place the brine in a suitable stoppered flask and add 20 ml of 2.5% (by weight) APDC for each 100 ml of brine. Shake the sample for 10 min. Add 20 ml of MIBK for each 100 ml of brine. Shake the sample for 10 min. Place the sample in a separatory funnel for one hour. Separate the aqueous and organic phases, and centrifuge the aqueous phase adding the centrifuged, minor organic phase to that previously separated. The entire sample may be centrifuged if desired and suitable equipment is available.

The investigation of oil field brines required the analyzing of a large number of samples for many elements. This, in turn, required the storage of the extracted organic phase. Unfortunately, the organic phase proved unstable and precipitate formed in less than one hour after extraction. This precipitate required that the organic phase be converted to a low pH aqueous solution because storage was necessary. The next step thus consisted of evaporating the organic phase slowly to a dry residue using infra red lamps. Add 25 ml concentrated nitric acid to the residue and slowly boil until about 2 ml of solution remain. Add sufficient double distilled water to bring the sample to a final volume. Determine the concentration of trace metals against low pH aqueous standards. See also Galle (1971).

A test was performed in 5% sodium chloride solution to determine the amount extracted, and the results (in % recovered) are as follows: Bi (100), Cd (96), Cr (100), Co (100), Cu (100), Fe (100), Mn (83), Mo (77), Ni (100), Pb (100), Zn (100), Ca (0), Ba (0), K(0), Li (0), Mg (0), Rb (0), Sr (0).

The analysis of fresh waters for trace elements has become more critical because of pollution problems currently under study by numerous researchers. ANGINO et al. (1969) and GALLE and ANGINO (1968) have developed methods for a number of elements in fresh waters. In their method, water samples were collected in one-liter polyethylene bottles which had been previously triple washed with a 50% v/v HNO_3 solution followed by a washing with deionized water. The water samples were passed through a 1.2 μ millipore filter to separate suspended material. The choice of this pore size was to allow a filtration time of less than one hour. Normally, 0.45 μ filter was used. Ten milliliters of HCl were added to 500 ml of filter water and evaporated to approximately 10 ml. This solution was transferred to a 50 ml volumetric flask and diluted to volume with distilled deionized water. The method was proven to be routinely useful in the range of 0.01–1 p.p.m. for Co, Ni, Li; 0.01–10 p.p.m. for Mn, Sr, Zn, and Si; and 0.01–100 p.p.m. for Ca, Mg, and Fe. The coefficient of variation for each element was: Co, 6% at 0.08 p.p.m.; Fe, 5% at 0.06 p.p.m.; Li, 10% at 0.01 p.p.m.; Mn, 2.5% at 0.02 p.p.m.; and Sr, 7% at 0.08 p.p.m. respectively.

CHAO (1969) has reported a method for determining gold in waters by a combination of anion exchange and atomic absorption. As is the case for Ag, Au absorbs on the sides of sample containers and must be acidified to pH 1 with hydrochloric acid with the addition of 50 mg of Br/l to prevent absorption. Under such conditions an AGl-X8 anion exchange resin collects gold quantitatively from water. The gold may be removed from the resin by use of an acetone–nitric acid–water mixture (volume ratio = 100:5:5). The acetone is then evaporated in a constant temperature water bath leaving Au and HNO_3.

Extraction from the HNO_3 was performed into MIBK, containing an additional 0.25 ml of 1% bromine water per 50 ml nitric acid solution.

Efforts to determine such pollutants as Pb have resulted in attempts to complex lead and then extract it into organic solution. One of these methods has been described by CHAKRABARTI (1967b). When lead in aqueous solution is complexed as K_2PbI_6 and the complex extracted into methyl isopropyl ketone, a three-fold increase in sensitivity relative to the aqueous solution of lead was obtained. A 178 mm-long adaptor on the top of a Beckman Integral Aspirated burner (oxy-hydrogen) was used. A sensitivity (in p.p.m./1% absorption) of 0.007 and a standard deviation of 0.014 p.p.m. were obtained with a sample containing 0.1 p.p.m. lead. Interferences in the aqueous solution analysis of lead consisted of anions such as PO_4^{3-}, Cl^-, CO_3^{2-}, I^- and others as did high concentrations of various cations. The solvent extraction technique eliminated all interferences including the non-specific interferences of the cations by producing a uniform matrix for all samples and standard.

Another example of a trace element being studied from pollution aspects is Ag (WEST et al., 1967). The problem of Ag absorption onto container surfaces from water samples has been overcome by the use of EDTA. However, this requires analysis after complexing of Ag with EDTA, and the following method was developed. The analytical method was based on the preferential extraction of Ag from the Ag–EDTA complex using an ester solution of dithizone (0.05 g of diphenylthiocarbazone per 100 ml of ethyl propionate; this solution is stable indefinitely). The ester–dithizone–silver extract can be aspirated into an air–acetylene flame directly. The addition of 1 ml of acetone to the 10 ml ethyl–propionate-dithizone–silver fraction following extraction provided a homogeneous solution that yielded a very stable flame characteristic. The extraction coefficient is 19, thus establishing the validity of using only a single extraction in the procedure.

For waters containing 0.005–0.05 mg/l of silver, a 200 ml volume is required. Ten milliliters of the dithizone ethyl-propionate reagent are added; the sample is shaken for 1 min. Approximately 10 min. are required for separation of the aqueous and solvent phases. One milliliter of acetone is added to the sample extract in a test tube.

APPENDIX TO CHAPTER 6

Ore Analysis

INTRODUCTION

Analyses for many ore metals have been reported in the literature since our first publication in 1967. However, in most instances we have witnessed refinement of existing methods and techniques and a lowering of sensitivity levels. As a consequence, we have decided, with exceptions, in this appended and up-dated printing of our book to treat primarily those elements for which few if any, reliable techniques were available in 1967. Additionally, we have introduced a few new methods for those elements of major economic interest (e.g., Au and Pt). The elements are considered, insofar as possible, in the same order as in the first edition.

GOLD

Little has been reported in the literature concerning the use of solvent extraction in the presence of insoluble residues which cause the formation of large emulsions. A technique that should have general application has been described by LAW and GREEN (1969). In the extraction of aqua regia-dissolved gold in solution contact with insoluble matter remaining from large (500 g) samples, most of the MIBK (methyl isobutyl ketone) is held in an emulsion, one of several phases present in such solvent extraction methods.

The validity of the method to be described is dependent upon the MIBK in the small clear phase developed being the same as the composition of MIBK droplets in the emulsion. This is expected to be true because the emulsion is of a mechanical nature. The volume change of MIBK during extraction was also investigated. Reagent grade chemicals can be used as purchased. The procedure is simple and straightforward.

Weigh approximately 500 g of 100 mesh gold ore sample into an 800 ml beaker and place in a cool muffle furnace. Subsequently, raise the furnace temperature to 550°C and hold for one hour. Cool carefully and add 160 ml of concentrated HCl and 40 ml of concentrated HNO_3. Cover the beaker with a ribbed watch glass and evaporate with occasional stirring to a damp condition. Add equilibrated, dilute HCl, stirring to break up lumps, and transfer the solution and residue to a 1000 ml screw top Erlenmeyer flask. Complete the transfer with equilibrated dilute HCl. Add HCl until the total volume in the flask is about 900 ml. Pipette 50 or 100 ml of MIBK into the flask and shake for 2 min. An emulsion forms at this step. Add enough equilibrated dilute HCl to bring the upper level of the contents into the neck of the flask and mix thoroughly. Shake and swirl contents until 5–10 ml of clear MIBK separates above the emulsion. Run atomic absorption readings on Au standards and MIBK extracts from the samples. Convert the values obtained to micrograms of gold per ml and calculate the gold concentration of the sample on the basis of volume of MIBK added.

Comparison of results with other methods, using U.S. Geological Survey gold-quartz standards, was good. One decided advantage of this method is that it provides a means for accurately measuring small quantities of gold in large samples of low grade ores.

GROENEWALD (1969) presents an alternative solvent extraction method for the determination of gold in solution. He examined the extraction of gold complex ions into diisobutyl ketone containing either trioctylamine or trioctyl methyl ammonium chloride. In the rapid determination of gold (III) in aqueous solution the procedure of extracting the gold (III) from an aqueous chloride or cyanide solution into diisobutyl ketone containing the quaternary ammonium salt is recommended. The gold content in the organic phase can subsequently be determined by atomic absorption.

The extraction of Au (III) from aqueous chloride solution is quantitative at pH values up to 4, and from cyanide solution at pH values as high as 10. This is valid at aqueous to organic phase volume ratios of 100:1. Gold concentrations of $2.5 \cdot 10^{-4}$ to $5 \cdot 10^{-8}$ M (50–0.01 mg/l) can be measured.

Application of the method to the analyses of Au bearing ores demonstrated the method to be free of interferences from most elements. Comparisons with the fire-assay techniques are good.

A somewhat similar method, using an organic solvent containing a quaternary ammonium salt is described by GROENEWALD (1968) for the determination of gold (I) in cyanide solutions. The precision and accuracy of this technique is reported to be good. It too is reported to be free of other elemental interferences.

THOMPSON et al. (1968) present a rapid analytical method for the determination of gold in geologic materials. Their direct and simple technique allows up to 100 samples a day to be analyzed by a "cold" method that yields a sensitivity of 0.002 p.p.m.

TABLE XXXVIII

COMPARISON OF GOLD VALUES OBTAINED BY ATOMIC ABSORPTION METHODS AND BY CONVENTIONAL GRAVIMETRIC FIRE-ASSAY METHOD

Gold (p.p.m.)			*Sample description*
gravimetric	*Atomic absorption*		*and locality*
fire-assay	*fire-assay*	*cyanide*	
4.8	4.8	4.3	Jefferson County, Mont., sulfide ore, White Pine Mine
10.3	11	10	channel sample, Gold Anchor mine, Clear Creek County, Colo.
13.7	16	15	pyrite, Belly Mine, Okanogan County, Wash.
15.8	18	14	quartz pyrite ore, Phoenix mine, Clear Creek County, Colo.
16.5	15	16	quartz vein, Okanogan County, Wash.
26.4	27	25	mineralized quartzite, Okanogan County, Wash.

Two methods, based on a marriage of atomic absorption and cyanide and fire-assay procedures, for the measurement of traces of gold in geologic materials are described in considerable detail by HUFFMAN et al. (1967). By either method concentrations as low as 50 p.p.b. of gold can be determined in 15 g samples. Table XXXVIII gives comparisons using these methods.

BAUXITE

Concentrations of aluminum, silicon, and titanium in bauxite can be ascertained in a nitrous oxide–acetylene flame by a method described by BOWMAN and WILLIS (1967). Bauxite solutions are prepared as follows:

(*1*) Acid solutions: one gram of bauxite is heated to fuming with 50 ml of mixed acid (500 ml of 1:1 H_2SO_4, 100 ml of HNO_3, and 100 ml of 70% $HClO_4$). The solution is diluted to 500 ml with water after filtering off the silica residue.

(*2*) Alkaline solutions: one gram of bauxite is fused with 5.0 g NaOH, and the melt leached with 40 ml of water, filtered, and made up to 200 ml with water.

(*3*) Borate solutions: one gram of bauxite is fused in a platinum crucible with 5 g of a 2:1 mixture of Na_2CO_3 and $Na_2B_4O_7 \cdot 10\,H_2O$. The melt is dissolved in 100 ml of 1:1 HCl and the solution made up to 200 ml with water.

For determinations of Al the solutions were diluted to give an Al concentration of 100–150 mg/ml. Solution (*1*) was found to enhance Al absorption by approximately 20%, solution (*2*) enhanced absorption by 5% and solution (*3*) by only about 3%. Fe, Si, and Ti did not interfere in any of the solutions. Results are good with all solutions.

Silicon determination requires a relatively luminous nitrous oxide–acetylene flame with considerable emission. Reproducible results are obtained using type (*3*) solutions. Results compare well with Si determined gravimetrically.

In the determination of Ti it was found that Fe had no effect, but that Al and H_2SO_4 enhanced Ti absorption by a factor slightly more than two. Al in the borate fusion enhanced the determination of Ti by about 30%. Results of acid solution and borate fusion compare well with those determined colorimetrically.

Use of these methods and a nitrous oxide–acetylene flame allows satisfactory determination of these elements all of which have previously been difficult even with atomic absorption techniques. LANGMYHR and PAUS (1968c) present another approach for analysis of bauxite, using an HF decomposition technique.

IRIDIUM

A fusion technique for the determination of iridium in a multi-component, precious metal concentrate was developed by VAN LOON (1969). The method is as follows: weigh an appropriate weight of sample (0.10 g recommended) into a 25 ml nickel crucible. Moisten the sample with a few drops of water and add 5 ml of HF. Expel all the HF and silica by heating. Using a glass rod, mix an excess of sodium peroxide (approx. 2.0 g for a 0.1 g sample) with the residue. Clean the rod of any sample material. Sinter the material over a flame for 30 min. and fuse at red heat for 5 min. Cool the crucible and residue and place in a 150 ml covered beaker. Fill the crucible with water and heat the beaker on a hotplate for 5 min. and wash the crucible contents into the beaker. Add 5 ml of 10% HCl to the crucible and reheat the beaker. Again, rinse the solution into the partially covered 150 ml beaker. Slowly acidify the beaker solution with concentrated HCl and then evaporate to 5 ml.

Add two ml of concentrated HNO_3 and allow aqua regia digestion to continue until *violent* bubbling ceases. Destroy most of the nitrates by successive additions of concentrated HCl followed by evaporation after each addition. Dilute the solution to about 50% final volume and filter into a 100 ml volumetric flask. Add enough Cu to make a final solution of at least 500 g/ml. Dilute the solution to volume with water.

Standards for comparison can be made by combining an aliquot of standard solution (with sufficient Cu and Na solution) to make final concentrations of 500 and 1000 p.p.m. respectively, and an amount of HCl similar to that in the samples. Determinations are made using the 2850Å iridium line. No advantage is gained by using a nitrous oxide–acetylene flame rather than an acetylene–air one.

A complex series of interferences can occur; the addition of Cu and Na to sample and standards, however, removes interferences due to base and other platinum metals.

Ca and Mg must be kept below 600 p.p.m. to give a solution free from interference. Iridium can be determined to 5 mg/ml using the method of VAN LOON.

BERYLLIUM

A procedure for determination of beryllium in a beryl ore is given in THOMAS and CHUMNONG (1969). In brief the method involves the fusion of a sample with an appropriate flux (e.g. NaOH or KOH), acidification, and analysis. The analyses are made in a nitrous oxide–acetylene flame, using the 2348 Å Be line.

Six 0.250 g samples of finely crushed and dried (3 h at 110°C) beryl are fused with 1.5 g of KOH in zirconium crucibles. Cool the melts and dissolve in 100 ml of distilled water and acidify with 15 ml concentrated HNO_3. The solution can be clarified by the addition of 10 ml of 10% H_2O_2. Make up the solutions to 500 ml in standard volumetric flasks. Beryllium standards are prepared by dilution of a stock 500 p.p.m. solution of Be metal in dilute HNO_3. Make the solutions 3% (v/v) with respect to HNO_3. These same solutions contained 3000 p.p.m. KOH, 150 p.p.m. Si, and 50 p.p.m. Al.

Both Si and Al interfere with the determination of Be, causing a depressed absorbance and would have to be added to Be standards if great accuracy is desired. Potassium should be present in standards at a level similar to that in the analytical solution. Accuracy and precision obtained by this method are acceptable, with the latter exceeding 1% relative. This rapid technique can determine Be in the range of 0.5–15% Be (1.5–45% BeO).

PLATINUM

Potential ores of low concentrations of platinum metals in geologic materials of different types have become of increasing interest to the mining industry as mining and processing procedures have improved. Analytical difficulties in most methods for the determination of Pt led SWINDER (1968) to develop an atomic absorption method for this metal.

Standards are prepared from analytical grade reagents; samples are prepared by crushing and pulverizing to pass a 100 mesh sieve. Weigh out 5.0 g of the powered sample, place in 200 ml beakers, and add 25 ml of aqua regia. Cover the beakers and leach the samples at 95–100°C for 1.5 h, then remove the covers and take to dryness. Without removing the beakers from the hotplate, add 25 ml of concentrated grade HCl, cover the beakers and warm for an additional 10 min.

Upon cooling, transfer the samples to 100 ml volumetric flasks and dilute to volume with deionized water. Shake thoroughly and filter through Whatman No. 1 filter paper into 100 ml beakers. Where the metals do not occur as silicates, the filtrates can also be tested for Pb, Cu, Zn, Ag, Co, Ni, Mn, Mo.

Place 50 ml of sample solution into 125 ml separatory funnels and add 2 ml of 0.1 g/ml KI solution to each. Shake and allow to stand 5 min. Add 5 ml of MIBK to each sample and shake thoroughly for one minute. Allow the phases to separate and add another 2 ml of KI solution. Let the solutions stand for 5 min. and shake for one minute. After 15 min. shake again for one minute and allow the phases to separate. Run the organic fraction against previously prepared standards. Optimum results can be obtained when the organic phase contains between 0 and 10 mg/ml Pt. The method has not been tested where the Pt content exceeds 1 troy ounce/ton in ore. Pt was determined using the 2659 Å line. As little as 0.02 mg/ml Pt in 25% HCl has been effectively extrated and determined by this procedure. Normal ore samples provide an interference-free analysis for Pt using this procedure.

MERCURY

A procedure reported by HATCH and OTT (1968) outlines an extremely sensitive and accurate method for the determination of mercury down to the one p.p.b. level in solution. A simple reduction–aeration scheme is used to produce and introduce Hg vapor into a closed system where absorption of the 2537 Å line is monitored in a quartz windowed cell.

The procedure for rock samples is a variation of that used for analyzing Hg in Co and Ni metal. Add 25 ml of concentrated H_2SO_4 to 1–4 g of finely crushed material in a 250 ml roundbottom flask. *Carefully* add three 1 ml additions of 50% H_2O_2 solution to flask. Provide enough time for decomposition of peroxide between additions. Gently heat the flask to decompose any remaining peroxide and then cool to 20°C. Carefully add 100 ml of water and 5% potassium permanganate solution until a permanent pink color is obtained. Cool to 20°C and add 20 ml of mixed sodium chloride–hydroxylamine sulfate solution. Add 10 ml of stannous sulfate and immediately attach to an aeration apparatus (see HATCH and OTT, 1968). Aerate the solution according to the procedure prescribed in HATCH and OTT (1968) and measure the absorption of the Hg vapor. Few interferences exist under the procedure discussed. Results obtained on U.S. Geological Survey Standard Rocks G–1 and W–1 compare favorably with accepted values.

BISMUTH

A comparison of existing methods for the determination of Bi in ores led HUSLER (1970) to conclude that dissolution of samples with HNO_3 was the most desirable for field work. Bi recoveries obtained by the atomic absorption analysis of different tungsten ores (scheelite and wolframite) compared well with other techniques. The procedure can be subdivided into three steps: (*1*) Standard preparation: dissolve 1.000 g pure Bi metal in 50 ml concentrated HNO_3 and dilute to one liter with ion-free water. Such a solution is stable for two months. The desired Bi standards can be obtained by dilution of the stock solution; (*2*) Sample preparations: a 0.5–1.0 g sample of –200 mesh is accurately weighed into a 250 ml beaker. To this is added 20 ml 1:1 nitric acid and the sample covered and digested for 20–30 min. at the boiling point with occasional stirring. Filter the sample through the equivalent of Whatman No. 1 filter paper into a 100 ml volumetric flask, while rinsing with 1% HNO_3. Dilute to 100 ml with distilled water, aspirate and measure concentration by comparison with a standard curve; (*3*) Analyses can be made using an aspiration rate of 7 ml/min. at a wavelength of 2231 Å, appropriate current and slit settings, and in an air–acetylene flame. Results obtainable are comparable with other methods.

The presence of bismuth is a key indicator in geochemical prospecting for tungsten deposits which are commonly associated with bismuth. Bismuth determination is relatively free from most chemical interferences. No interference was noted from at least 2000 mg/l of Cu, Fe, Mg, Mn, Na, Pb, or Zn, or from 200 mg/1 of Al, As, Ba, Cu, Mo, Sb, Si, Sr, Te, V, or W when added to 20 mg/l Bi solutions. Minor interferences are noted with Ca.

TUNGSTEN

A direct method for the measurement of tungsten in wolframite is presented by THOMAS et al. (1969). These authors obtained good results using phosphoric acid solution with added potassium, 500 ± 0.2 mg samples of −100 mesh are dried at 110°C for 2 h. and mixed with 3 g of KOH pellets in a zirconium crucible. Heat gently at first to drive off the water, then more strongly until attaining red heat. Hold at this point for 2–3 minutes with agitation to ensure complete fusion. Cool and disperse the fused melt with 150 ml of hot water. Subsequent to cooling to room temperature, 40 ml of 50% H_3PO_4 and 10 ml of 10% H_2O_2 are added to dissolve any hydroxides. Make up the clear solutions to 500 ml. Appropriate standard solutions can be prepared as needed.

Determinations of tungsten can be obtained with either the 2551 or 4008 Å lines, the former being the more sensitive. A fuel-rich nitrous oxide–acetylene flame is required. Some difficulty can be encountered with the solution technique unless care is employed. Phosphoric acid is more suitable than sulfuric; however, some decrease in absorbance will occur owing to the effects of phosphoric acid.

The KOH used in the fusion step, actually causes an enhancement up to levels of 2000 p.p.m. K, after which no significant change is noted. SiO_2 has a minor effect on 500 p.p.m. W in a 10,000 p.p.m. K and 5% H_3PO_4 solution; a decrease in absorbance on 500 p.p.m. W and 5% H_3PO_4 solution is noted with an increase in Fe content from 0–10,000 p.p.m. A satisfactory precision is available with this method. Close monitoring of methodology improves the precision.

IRON

Using the hydrofluoric acid decomposition technique that they developed, LANGMYHR and PAUS (1969c) present a method for the analysis of iron ores. Other elements that may be present in the ores and that can be determined are Si, Al, Mg, Ca, Ti and Mn. With minor modification Na, K, Cr, V, Ba, Zn, Cu, Ag and Ni can be incorporated into the analyses.

Preparation of the requisite primary standard is described in LANGMYHR and PAUS (1968a, p. 397). Secondary standards for each element to be analyzed can be prepared to cover the concentration ranges required.

The procedure is as follows: weigh 0.2000 g of sample, add by pipette 0.75 ml HCl, 0.25 ml HNO_3 and 5 ml of HF. The sample must be finely ground. Decomposition is obtained by heating the mixture in a PTFE (polytetrafluoroethylene) bomb for about 30 min. at a temperature of 110°C. Keep the bomb contents continually stirred with a magnetic stirrer. Cool the bomb to room temperature with running water and open. If further decomposition is required use the technique outlined by LANGMYHR and PAUS (1969a, p. 401, method 1).

Depending on the element to be determined, either a 3-slot Boling burner can be used (for acetylene–air flames) or a nitrous oxide burner (for nitrous oxide–acetylene flame). Results obtained using these techniques, when compared with appropriate British chemical standards, compare quite well.

APPENDIX TO CHAPTER 7

Rock and Mineral Analysis

SILICATE ROCKS

A compilation of analytical data for nine silicate mineral and rock reference samples is given in LANGMYHR and PAUS (1969d). The elements considered were Si, Al, Mg, Ca, Na, K, Ti, Mn, total Fe, and H_2O. Determinations were made by a scheme reported in LANGMYHR and PAUS (1968a). According to these authors, the decomposition of silicate rocks by hydrofluoric acid, followed by determination of metallic elements by atomic absorption spectrometry has not been utilized fully for the analysis of inorganic siliceous materials. Their technique was designed for the analysis of most types of inorganic siliceous materials decomposable by 40% HF and containing Si, Al, Fe, Mg, Ca, Na, and K as main constituents. Many other metallic elements can be determined by the scheme presented.

The method is based on taking a 5.0 g sample and grinding it to pass a 120 mesh screen. The sample is air dried, 0.20 g weighed out, and digested by 5 ml of 38–40% HF in a plastic vessel appropriate for use at temperatures above 100°C. For some evaporations polytetrafluoroethylene is required. Different equipment is used for digestion below and above the boiling point (112°C) of the azeotropic mixture of HF and H_2O (38.26% HF). A bomb technique is required for temperatures above the boiling point of 38.26° HF.

Appropriate reagents and standard solutions can be prepared as needed. In practice four variants on the decomposition scheme are possible, depending on the nature of the siliceous material and whether silicon is or is not to be determined. Subsequent to decomposition, a boric acid solution (50 ml of saturated solution) is added to dissolve any precipitated fluorides. The solution is then diluted to 100 ml with distilled water. Prior to using this technique, one should consult the original paper for details. Chemical interferences are reported but can be eliminated or compensated for.

All measurements reported by Langmyrhr and Paus were made with a Perkin–Elmer 303 model atomic absorption spectrometer. A 3-slot Boling burner was used for the acetylene–air flames; a nitrous oxide burner was employed for an acetylene–nitrous oxide flame.

Using further modifications of their basic decomposition techniques (four approaches are outlined: LANGMYHR and PAUS, 1968a, p.397), methods for the analysis of bauxite, siliceous limestones, ferrosilicon, and feldspars are presented respectively in LANGMYHR and PAUS (1968c, 1969a,b,c).

A technique for partial analysis of silicate rocks by atomic absorption spectrometry is given by BELT (1967); while quite dependable as far as it goes, it has been superseded to a considerable degree by the work of BERNAS (1968) who devised a fluoboric–boric acid system that provides a good decomposition medium and a dependable salt-free single matrix system. A specially designed vessel manufactured from Teflon (DuPont trademark) is the key to the decomposition step and is the reason for the method's effectiveness.

Both the decomposition and reaction steps should be carried out in a hood. Transfer 50 mg (if V is to be analyzed – 300 mg) of a typical –150 mesh size sample to one of the specially designed decomposition vessels (these vessels are available commercially) and add 0.5 ml of aqua regia as a wetting agent. Be certain the sample is wetted thoroughly. Add 3.0 ml HF (48%) and close the vessel. Place the crucible, with no tilting, into a 110°C drying oven for 30–40 min. After heating, allow to cool to room temperature.

Transfer the decomposed sample solution, using 4–6 ml of distilled water, into a 50 ml polystyrene vial. A quantitative transfer of any precipitated fluoride is imperative; do not let the volume exceed 10 ml. To this, add 2.8 g of boric acid and stir with a Teflon rod to hasten the dissolution of the boric acid. At this point add 5–10 ml of distilled water.

Precipitated fluorides, if present, should dissolve at this point. Dilute to about 40 ml, and transfer the clear solution to a 100 ml volumetric flask, fill to volume, and store in polyethylene container.

Do not allow the sample solution to remain in contact with glass for greater than 2 h.

Any constituent can be determined from this solution. Solutions can be aspirated into an air–acetylene flame and concentrations determined from appropriate standards and graphs. The method was tested by treating four silicate rock standards as unknowns. Standards used were granite G-1, diabase W-1, australite, and philippinite. Results agree within 1.3% relative or better for major elements and 4% relative or better for minor components. No inter-element interferences for Fe, Si, Al, Ti, V, Ca, Mg, Na, or K were noted. The matrix system (HBF_4-H_3BO_3-ionic contents of silicate) is discussed in some detail in the original article. This method of BERNAS (1968) has much to recommend it and undoubtedly will find considerable use in the analyses of silicate rocks.

Alumina and silica in silicate rocks

Another of the more difficult analyses to perform is that of the quantitative determination of alumina and silica in silicate rocks and minerals. KATZ (1968) presents a NaOH fusion technique that is both more complete and better than the well known Na_2CO_3 fusion in platinum. A nitrous oxide–acetylene flame is used. The analytical lines used for SiO_2 and Al_2O_3 were respectively 2516 Å and 3093 Å.

About 0.5 g of sample (–200 mesh) is weighed into a 100 ml Ni crucible. To this is added about 1.0 g NaOH pellets (AR grade) and the crucible heated uncovered at a low bunsen flame until the NaOH melts. Heat slightly and swirl until a clear melt is obtained. Subsequent to cooling, add about 50 ml of doubly distilled water stirring carefully with a Ni spatula. Pour off the water into a polyethylene 500 ml beaker and add a second 50 ml of doubly distilled water to the crucible. Transfer the crucible to a hotplate and heat carefully with no boiling until the fused mass loosens. It is then placed in the same beaker containing the poured out solution. Place the beaker with the several washings from the crucible onto a magnetic stirrer and mix the contents until all fused solids have dissolved. Without stopping the mixing, slowly add 50 ml concentrated HCl until the solution is distinctly acid. Transfer the solution to a 500 ml flask, cool to room temperature and dilute with water, shake, and quickly transfer to a 500 ml well-stoppered plastic bottle. Several samples can be run simultaneously.

For silica determination, take 25 ml of solution and dilute to volume with water in a 100 ml volumetric flask. This should be quickly transferred to an appropriate small plastic bottle. For alumina, take 50 ml of sample solution, place in a 100 ml volumetric flask, add 3 ml of a 4% KCl solution (in water) and make up the solution to volume.

Standard solutions are prepared as needed. Results using accepted standards show good agreement with reported data. The technique is rapid and simple and warrants further use and evaluation.

Useful variations of the hydrofluoric acid dissolution technique for the determination of Mg, Li, Zn, Fe, Ca, Na, K, and total Fe are described in two papers by ABBEY (1967, 1968). These articles also present a good discussion of interferences and tests for interferences to be expected for these elements and means of coping with them. A potentially useful new scheme for precise rock analysis is also reported.

Strontium in silicates

One of the more difficult elements to determine by wet chemical methods is strontium. Large variation of strontium values are reported for "standard granite" G–1 and G–2 and "standard diabase" W–1. Using a simple and straightforward technique, HUFFMAN and MENSIK (1967) obtained good reproducibility of results. The procedure is based on the decomposition of 1.0 g of rock samples with HF, HNO_3, and $HClO_4$ acids (Perkin–Elmer methods manual), fuming to drive off fluoride, and preparation of a 100 ml 5% HCl solution (v/v). Appropriate standards and calibration curves are made as needed. Strontium determinations were made using an air–acetylene flame with a Perkin–Elmer 303 model spectrophotometer set at a wave length of 4607 Å.

Bismuth in altered rocks

Trace amounts of bismuth are often associated with several important ore minerals and ore bearing rocks. The presence or absence of trace amounts of Bi can serve as a guide to the location of concealed ore deposits. A straightforward procedure for the determination of small amounts of Bi in altered rocks is discussed in WARD and NAKAGAWA (1967). Weigh 0.5 g of finely powered sample into a 16 x 150 mm test tube and add 5 ml of concentrated HNO_3. A small Teflon-covered magnet is inserted into the mixture and the tube plus contents are placed on an aluminum heating block.

The block is then placed on a hotplate equipped with a rotating magnet and the contents of the test tube heated, stirring until the mixture boils gently. Heating and stirring should be continued for 30 min. Remove the tube and contents from the heating block, cool, and dilute with water to the 10 ml mark on the tube. Either centrifuge or allow solids to settle to bottom of tube. Atomize the supernatant solution into an air–acetylene flame–Boling burner combination. The Bi content is determined using the 2231 Å line.

Fine grinding of the samples results in better precision, especially if small starting samples are used. Observed accuracy, based on comparison of the results obtained with other methods, is good.

Tellurium in rocks

Tellurium in rocks can be determined by a simple procedure reported by NAKAGAWA and THOMPSON (1968). The 2140 Å Te line is used. Briefly, 5.0 g of pulverized sample is dissolved in a hydrobromic acid–bromine mixture. Te is selectively extracted into methyl isobutyl ketone and the organic extract atomized into an air–acetylene flame.

No interferences at ratios of element:tellurium of 1:2000 were noted for Pb, Zn, Ca, and Sb. Large amounts of Fe interfered. Precision and accuracy tests indicate that the method is satisfactory for geochemical exploration.

TRACE ELEMENTS IN CALCIUM SULFATE MINERALS

A procedure for the determination of trace elements in calcium sulfate minerals using organic solvents is presented by HUSLER and CRUFT (1969). In their scheme, the sample solution, with Cd as a collector, is treated with 8–hydroxyquinoline, tannic acid, and thionalide, and the pH adjusted to 5.9. Co, Ni, Mo, Cu, Sn, Pb, Zn, Ti, V, Cr, Ga, Ge, Be, Al, Fe, Cd, Ag, Au, and Pd are precipitated quantitatively at this pH. Keeping the pH below 6.1 eliminates Ca; at a pH of 5.1 8–hydroxyquinoline precipitated most of above listed elements. Adding tannic acid to the 8–hydroxyquinoline makes the recovery of V, Cr, Be, Sn, and Ge quantitative. Pb and Sn are obtained by treating with thionalide and 8–hydroxyquinoline.

Upon precipitating the organic–metallic complexes, they can be collected and redissolved with acetone and nitric acid, digested and then diluted to known volumes. Ti and V, were analyzed in an acetylene–nitrous oxide flame. Small amounts of Ca interfere with the determination of V and Ti, but the interference can be removed by adding a small amount of Ca to the samples and standards to assure the presence of Ca above a critical minimum level.

APPENDIX TO CHAPTER 8

Recent Sediments

TRACE ELEMENTS

In their study of Recent sediments from the Indian Ocean BENDER and SCHULTZ (1969) outline a useful method for measuring Fe, Mn, Ni, Co, Cu, Zn and $CaCO_3$ by atomic absorptions spectrometry. Approximately 5 g samples were selected from the tops of piston cores and powdered. One gram aliquots of each were separated and leached. A working solution was obtained by leaching the sample with 10 ml of HCl and fuming with 10 ml of $HF-HClO_4$. This process was repeated until no visible residue remained.

The solution is taken nearly to dryness and diluted with distilled water to 50 ml; Ni, Co and Cu are determined directly while Mn, Zn and Fe are determined following further dilution. Concentrations are measured by comparing the elemental atomic absorbency for each sample with standard absorbance curves. Standards were dissolved and analyzed with the same procedure. W–1 was the standard. Calcium carbonate concentrations are obtained by dissolving the calcium carbonate from an aliquot of powdered sediment sample with acetic acid. These solutions are then diluted to a satisfactory volume and calcium determined by atomic absorption.

The accuracy and precision of this method while not the best does provide useful estimates for comparison with other materials.

Trace elements in interstitial waters of Recent sediments

BROOKS et al. (1968) describe a method for determining K, Mg, Na, Ca and Sr directly on diluted samples of interstitial waters of marine sediments by atomic absorption spectrometry. Dilute samples of surface water were used as standard, since concentrations of the above elements were not uniform. The trace consituents of the interstitial waters can be determined in the following manner.

Two hundred 50 ml samples of interstitial waters are acidified with doubly distilled, constant boiling HCl to reduce the pH to 4.0. Twenty-five ml of methyl isobutyl ketone (MIBK) are added to each sample and 5 ml of 1% ammonium pyrolidine dithiocarbonate (APDC). The APDC was purified by equilibration with an equal volume of MIBK followed by separation and rejection of the organic phase. The mixtures are then brought to equilibrium for 30 min. on an agitating rack. The phases can be separated with separatory funnels. Standards consisted of 250 ml of previously extracted sea water samples containing incremental amounts of the added ions. These are then extracted into 20 ml quantities of MIBK after addition of APDC as described previously. The small amount of solvent provided for the solubility of MIBK in the unequilibrated original samples. Standards and samples are analyzed by atomic absorption spectrometry using high intensity lamps for Co, Ni and Fe. For greater details of the method refer to the article by BROOKS et al. (1967).

Trace elements in carbonate rocks

A sensitive method for the trace element analysis of carbonate rocks using APDC–MIBK extraction and atomic absorption spectrometry is described by ST. JOHN (1970). The technique is made possible through the use of a sodium hydroxide–ammonium chloride buffer and 20% HCl solution. Certain details of the procedure are critical; consequently, for optimum results, a review of the original paper is recommended.

Analyses were made of several samples of *Millepora* sp. from the Coral Sea for Co, Cd, Cu, Ni, Zn, Fe, and Pb. 75 g (weighed accurately) of sample material are placed in a 2000 ml beaker and covered. To this, 100 ml of HCl is added quantitatively and the sample allowed to digest for 4 h. Subsequent to digestion, the acid wash of the sample is quantitatively washed through a 0.45 μ membrane filter (prefiltering is required). Residual carbonate is washed, dried and weighed and the dissolved sample weight calculated.

Appropriate standard and buffer solutions are necessary. Ten ml of 2% w/v APDC solution in water are added to each sample and standard. Chelation is carried out at a pH of 3.75 with manual shaking for one minute. To each sample and standard 10 ml of MIBK is added with extraction completed by manually shaking for one minute. Separation occurs in a few minutes. The MIBK phase can be aspirated directly into an atomic absorption spectrometer. A Techtron AA-4 Atomic Absorption Unit equipped with single element hollow-cathode tubes and a single-slot premix burner, was used with an air–C_2H_2 flame. Sensitivity of the method is in the parts-per-billion range. The method is also applicable to the analysis of fresh, sea, brine, or interstitial waters.

APPENDIX TO CHAPTER 9

Isotopes

LEAD ISOTOPES

A potentially useful method for the determination of ^{206}Pb, ^{207}Pb, and ^{208}Pb isotopes has been described by BRIMHALL (1969). Studies on the differential atomic absorption of lead show that sufficient differences exist in the hyperfine spectrum of lead attributable to the isotopes that a potentially useful method for the measurement of lead isotopes can be derived. Although no experiments have been performed, differential atomic absorption probably occurs for the ^{204}Pb isotope as well. The technique uses special hollow-cathode tubes enriched respectively in ^{206}Pb, ^{207}Pb, and ^{208}Pb. This coupled with appropriately enriched aqueous standards forms the basis of the method.

With minor modification the method employs standard atomic absorption equipment. Analyses of samples with known concentrations of lead isotopes give results which differ about 3% from known values. Precision for geochronological studies surpasses that of the Pb-alpha method, but not that of mass spectrometric techniques. Use of high intensity lamps and appropriate preconcentration procedures will probably allow increased sensitivity of the method.

Instrumental response is dependent upon isotopic differences, although they are not independent of one another. Using appropriate solutions and controls and measurements, one can set up a series of simultaneous linear equations in three unknowns, solutions of which lead to determination of concentrations of Pb isotopes in an unknown, providing samples were measured under the same experimental conditions as the standards. It is assumed that the peak height for any given standard with respect to a given lamp is the summation of three terms, each of which is the product of the concentration of a specific isotope in the standard multiplied by a constant associated with the isotope. Techniques for carrying out these analyses are not exceedingly involved. Still another approach to the determination of Pb isotope ratios by atomic absorption is described by KIRDHOF (1969).

JOSEPH et al. (1969) described a method for determining the isotopic concentration of ^{40}K and ^{87}Rb in various types of samples. The technique, based upon pertinent radiation and natural abundance data for these isotopes, offers a satisfactory method of estimation of ^{40}K and ^{87}Rb.

Determination of non-metals

SOME ADVANCES

Since the original edition of this book, some advances have been made in the determination of non-metals either by their interfering properties during the analysis for metals or by their precipitation and subsequent metal-analysis followed bv calculation of the non-metal.

Sulfate and orthophosphate cause a decrease in Ca absorption proportional to the anion concentration, as do proteins and glucose. The use of standard curves for the degree of interference in the Ca analysis thus can lead to determination of the amount of interfering material by determination of the decrease or increase in Ca absorption. Another type of determination is by solvent extraction of an equivalent amount of metal, for example, adding excess metal to a solution containing APDC and then determining the amount of metal in the extracted portion is a method of analysis for the chelating agent. A very detailed study of this type of approach to chemical analysis has been given by CHRISTIAN and FELDMAN (1968). They also considered another type of indirect determination, such as that in which a metal ion is oxidized or reduced followed by a solvent extraction of the oxidized–reduced form. They were able to use this approach to determine I^- and IO_3^- in various solutions.

The determination of anions by precipitation with the metal has been used to determine Cl^- (with Ag ion), S as $BaSO_4$, orthophosphate (with Mo). Mixtures of P and Si have been determined by precipitation with Mo as have been some non-ionic surfactants. These approaches are referenced in CHRISTIAN and FELDMAN (1970) and in MAVRODINEANU (1970).

F^- depresses the absorption of Mg in an air–coal-gas flame. The depression is proportional to the F^- concentration. In the absence of interfering ions, principally SO_4^{2-} and phosphate, the effect can be used to determine F^-. An alternative, but less sensitive method, is based on the enhancement of Zr absorption by F^- in a nitrous oxide–acetylene flame (BOND and O'DONNELL, 1968).

References to the Appendix

ABBEY, S., 1967. Analysis of rocks and minerals by atomic absorption spectroscopy, 1. Determination of magnesium, lithium, zinc, and iron. *Geol. Surv. Can., Pap.*, 67-37, 35 pp.

ABBEY, S., 1968. Analysis of rocks and minerals by atomic absorption spectroscopy, 2. Determination of total iron, magnesium, calcium, sodium, and potassium. *Geol. Surv. Can., Pap.*, 68-20, 21 pp.

AMOS, M.D. and THOMAS, P.E., 1965. The determination of aluminum in aqueous solution by atomic absorption spectroscopy. *Anal. Chim. Acta*, 32: 139.

ANGINO, E.E., GALLE, O.K. and WAUGH, T.C., 1969. Fe, Mn, Ni, Co, Sr, Li, Zn, and SiO_2 in streams of the lower Kansas River basin. *Water Resour. Res.*, 5 (3): 698–705.

BARNES, JR., L., 1966. Determination of chromium in low alloy steels by atomic absorption spectroscopy. *Anal. Chem.*, 38: 1083.

BELT, JR., C., 1967. Partial analysis of silicate rocks by atomic absorption. *Anal. Chem.*, 39: 676–678.

BENDER, M.L. and SCHULTZ, C., 1969. The distribution of trace metals and cores from a traverse from the Indian Ocean. *Geochim. Cosmochim Acta*, 33: 292–297.

BENTLEY, E.M. and LEE, G.F. 1967. Determination of calcium in natural waters by atomic absorption spectrophotometry. *Environ. Sci. Technol.*, 1: 721–724.

BERNAS, B., 1968. A new method for decomposition and comprehensive analysis of silicates by atomic absorption spectrometry. *Anal. Chem.*, 40: 1682–1686.

BILLINGS, G.K. and RAGLAND, P.C., 1969. Atomic absorption spectrometry: geochemical techniques and problems. *Can. Spectros.*, 14 (1): 1–7.

BOETTNER, E.A. and GRUNDER, F.I., 1968. Water analysis by atomic absorption and flame emission spectroscopy. In: R.A. BAKER (Editor), *Trace Inorganics in Water. Adv. Chem. Ser.*, 73: 236–246.

BOKOWSKI, D.I., 1968. Rapid determination of beryllium by a direct reading atomic absorption spectrophotometer. *Am. Ind. Hyg. Assoc. J.*, 29 (5): 474–481.

BOND, A.M. and O'DONNELL, T.A., 1968. Determination of fluoride by atomic absorption spectrometry. *Anal. Chem.*, 40 (3): 560–563.

BOND, A.M. and WILLIS, J.B., 1968. Enhancement of zirconium atomic absorption by nitrogen-containing compounds and its use in the determination of ammonia. *Anal. Chem.*, 40 (14): 2087–2090.

BOWMAN, J.A. and WILLIS, J.B., 1967. Some applications of the nitrous oxide–acetylene flame in chemical analysis by atomic absorption spectrometry. *Anal. Chem.*, 39: 1210–1216.

BRIMHALL, W.H., 1969. Measurement of lead isotopes by differential atomic absorption. *Anal. Chem.*, 41: 1349–1351.

BROOKS, R.R., PRESLEY, B.J. and KAPLAN, I.R., 1967. The APDC–MIBK extraction system for the determination of trace elements in saline waters by atomic absorption spectrometry. *Talanta*, 14: 809–816.

BROOKS, R.R. PRESLEY, B.J. and KAPLAN, I.R., 1968. Trace elements in the interstitial waters of marine sediments. *Geochim. Cosmochim. Acta*, 32: 397–414.

BURRELL, D.C., 1968. Atomic absorption spectrophotometry in the field of marine research. *At. Absorpt. Newsl.*, 7: 65.

CHAKRABARTI, C.L., 1967a. The atomic absorption spectroscopy of tellurium. *Anal. Chim. Acta*, 39: 293.

CHAKRABARTI, C.L., 1967b. Determination of lead in aqueous and organic media by atomic absorption spectroscopy. *Appl. Spectros.*, 21 (3): 160–164.

CHAO, T.T., 1969. Determination of gold in waters in Nanogram Range by anion exchange in atomic absorption spectrophotometry. *Econ. Geol.*, 64: 287–290.

CHAU, Y.K. and WONG, P.Y., 1968. Determination of scandium in sea water by atomic absorption spectroscopy. *Talanta*, 15: 867.

CHRISTIAN, G.D. and FELDMAN, F.J., 1968. Determination of nonmetals by atomic absorption spectrophotometry. *Anal. Chim. Acta*, 40: 173.

CHRISTIAN, G.D. and FELDMAN, F.J., 1970. *Atomic Absorption Spectroscopy: Application in Agriculture, Biology and Medicine.* Wiley, New York, N.Y., 490 pp.

DOWLING, F.B., CHAKRABARTI, C.L. and LYLES, G.R., 1963. Atomic absorption spectroscopy of aluminum. *Anal. Chim. Acta*, 28: 392–394.

FABRICAND, B.P., IMBIMBO, E.S., and BERY, M.E., 1967. Atomic absorption analyses for Ca, Li, Mg, K, Rb, and Sr at two Atlantic Ocean stations. *Deep Sea Res.*, 14: 785–789.

FASSEL, V.A. and BECKER, D.A., 1969. Chemical or solute vaporization interferences in flame atomic emission and absorption spectrometry. *Anal. Chem.*, 41 (12): 1522–1526.

FISHMAN, M.J. and MIDGETT, M.R., 1968. Extraction techniques for the determination of cobalt, nickel, and lead in fresh water by atomic absorption. In: R.A. Baker (Editor), *Trace Inorganics in Water. Adv. Chem. Ser.* 73: 230–235.

GALLE, O.K., 1971. Determination of trace elements in brine by atomic absorption. *Appl. Spectrosc.*, 25: 664–667.

GALLE, O.K. and ANGINO, E.E., 1968. Trace elemental analysis of fresh water by atomic absorption. *Kans. Geol. Surv., Bull.*, 191: 3–7.

GROENEWALD, T., 1968. Determination of gold (I) in cyanide solutions by solvent extraction and atomic absorption spectrometry. *Anal. Chem.*, 40: 863–866.

GROENEWALD, T., 1969. Quantitative determination of gold in solution by solvent extraction and atomic absorption spectrometry. *Anal. Chem.*, 41: 1012–1015.

GUPTA, H.K.L., AMORE, F.J. and BOLTZ, D.F., 1968. The determination of gallium by atomic absorption spectrometry. *At. Absorpt. Newsl. Perkin-Elmer Corp.*, (76): 107–109.

HARRISON, W.W. and JULIANO, P.O., 1969. Effects of organic solvents on tin absorbance in an air–hydrogen flame. *Anal. Chem.*, 41 (8): 1016–1021.

HATCH, W.R. and OTT, W.L., 1968. Determination of sub-microgram quantities of mercury by atomic absorption spectrophotometry. *Anal. Chem.*, 40: 2085–2087.

HONMA, K., 1969. Measurement methods and devices for air-borne particulates. *Kukichowa Reito.*, 9 (1): 70–80.

HUFFMAN, JR., C. and MENSIK, J.D., 1967. Strontium content of some standard samples. *Appl. Spectrosc.*, 21: 125–126.

HUFFMAN, JR., C., MENSIK, J.D. and RILEY, L.B., 1967. Determination of gold in geologic materials by solvent extraction and atomic absorption spectrometry. *U.S. Geol. Surv., Circ.*, 544: 6 pp.

HUSLER, J.W., 1970. Atomic absorption determination of bismuth in soils, rocks, and ores. *At. Absorpt. Newsl., Perkin–Elmer Corp.*, 9: 31–32.

HUSLER, J.W. and CRUFT, E.F., 1969. Atomic absorption determination of trace elements in calcium sulfate minerals using an organic enrichment technique. *Anal. Chem.*, 41: 1688–1690.

HWANG, J.Y. and FELDMAN, F.J., 1970. Determination of atmospheric trace elements by atomic absorption spectroscopy. *Appl. Spectrosc.*, 24 (3): 371–374.

ISHII, T. and MUSHA, S., 1970. Rapid analysis of lead in automobile exhaust gas. *Bunseki Kagaku*, 19 (10): 1436–1437.

JAKUBIEC, R. and BOLTZ, D.F., 1969. An absorption spectrometric study of molybdogermanic acid. Methods for the determination of germanium. *Anal. Chem.*, 41: 78–81.

JONES, J.L. and EDDY, R.B., 1968. Determination of iron and nickel in water and brine by solvent extraction and atomic absorption spectroscopy. *Anal. Chim. Acta*, 43: 165.

JOSEPH, K.T., PARAMESWARAN, M. and SOMAN, S.D., 1969. Estimation of ^{40}K and ^{87}Rb in environmental samples using atomic absorption spectrophotometry. *At. Absorpt. Newsl., Perkin–Elmer Corp.*, 8 (6): 127–128.

JULIANO, P.O. and HARRISON, W.W., 1970. Atomic absorption interferences of tin. *Anal. Chem.*, 42 (1): 84–89.

JUNGREIS, E. and ANAVI, Z., 1969. Determination of sulphite ion (or sulphur dioxide) by atomic absorption spectroscopy. *Anal. Chim. Acta*, 45 (1): 190–192.

KAAHN, H.L., 1968. Principles and practice of atomic absorption. In: R.A. BAKER (Editor), *Trace Inorganics in Water. Adv. Chem. Ser. 73.*

KATZ, A., 1968. The direct and rapid determination of alumina and silica in silicate rocks and minerals by atomic absorption spectroscopy. *Am. Mineral.*, 53: 283–389.

KETTNER, H., 1969. Comparative determinations of lead in dust precipitations by the dithizon and atomic absorption spectrophotometric methods. *Schriftenr. Ver. Wasser Boden Lufthyg.* 29: 55–62.

KIRDHOF, H., 1969. Determination of isotope ratio for lead samples by atomic absorption. *Spectrochim. Acta*, 24 B: 235.

KOIRTYOHANN, S.R. and PICKETT, E.B., 1968. A new type of interference in atomic absorption or emission measurements with the premixed nitrous oxide–acetylene flame. *Anal. Chem.*, 40 (13): 2068–2070.

LANGMYHR, F.J. and PAUS, P.E., 1968a. The analysis of inorganic siliceous materials by atomic absorption spectrophotometry and the hydrofluoric acid decomposition technique, 1. The analysis of silicate rocks. *Anal. Chim. Acta*, 43: 397–408.

LANGMYHR, F.J. and PAUS, P.E., 1968b. The analysis of inorganic siliceous materials by atomic absorption spectrophotometry and the hydrofluoric acid decomposition technique, 2. The analysis of silica. *Anal. Chim. Acta*, 43: 506–507.

LANGMYHR, F.J. and PAUS, P.E., 1968c. The analysis of inorganic siliceous materials by atomic absorption spectrophotometry and the hydrofluoric acid decomposition technique, 3. The analysis of bauxite. *Anal. Chim. Acta*, 43: 508–510.

LANGMYHR, F.J. and PAUS, P.E., 1969a. The analysis of inorganic siliceous materials by atomic absorption spectrophotometry and the hydrofluoric acid decomposition technique, 4. The analysis of cements, clinkers, raw mixes, and siliceous limestones. *Anal. Chim. Acta*, 44: 445–446.

LANGMYHR, F.J. and PAUS, P.E., 1969b. The analysis of inorganic siliceous materials by atomic absorption spectrophotometry and the hydrofluoric acid decomposition technique, 6. The analysis of feldspars. *Anal. Chim. Acta*, 45: 176–179.

LANGMYHR, F.J. and PAUS, P.E., 1969c. The analysis of inorganic siliceous materials by atomic absorption spectrophotometry and the hydrofluoric acid decomposition technique, 7. The analysis of iron ores and slags. *Anal. Chim. Acta*, 45: 157–162.

LANGMYHR, F.J. and PAUS, P.E., 1969d. Hydrofluoric acid decomposition-atomic absorption analysis of nine silicate mineral and rock reference samples. *Anal. Chim. Acta*, 47: 371–373.

LAW, S.L. and GREEN, T.E., 1969. Solvent extraction in the presence of emulsion-forming residues. Application to atomic absorption determination of gold in low grade ores. *Anal. Chem.*, 41: 1008–1012.

LEVINE, J.R., MOORE, S.G. and LEVINE, S.L., 1970. Effect of potassium on determination of tin by atomic absorption spectrophotometry. *Anal. Chem.*, 42(3): 412–414.

MANNING, D.C. and CHABOT, H., 1968. The effect of acetylene containing acetone vapor in atomic absorption analysis. *At. Absorpt. Newsl., Perkin–Elmer Corp.*, 7 (5): 94–97.

MARX, J.Y. and WELCHER, G.G., 1970. Interelement interferences in atomic absorption analyses with a nitrous oxide–acetylene flame. *Anal. Chem.*, 42 (9): 1033–1040.

MAVRODINEANU, R. (Editor), 1970. *Analytical Flames Spectroscopy: Selected Topics.* Springer, New York, N.Y., 772 pp.

MENIS, O. and RAINS, T.C., 1969. Determination of arsenic by atomic absorption spectrometry with an electrodeless discharge lamp as a source of radiation. *Anal. Chem.*, 41 (7): 952–954.

NAKAGAWA, H.M. and THOMPSON, C.E., 1968. Atomic absorption determination of tellurium. *U.S. Geol. Surv., Prof. Pap.*, 600-B: 123–125.

RILEY, J.P. and TAYLOR, D., 1968. Chelating resins for the concentration of trace elements from sea water and their analytical use in conjunction with atomic absorption spectrometry. *Anal. Chim. Acta*, 40: 479.

SACHDEV, S.L. and WEST, B.W., 1970. Concentration of trace metals by solvent extraction and their determination by atomic absorption spectrophotometry. *Environ. Sci. Techn.*, 19 (9): 749–751.

SACHDEV, S.L., ROBINSON, J.W. and WEST, P.W., 1967. Determination of manganese, iron, cobalt, and nickel in air and water by atomic absorption spectroscopy. *Anal. Chim. Acta*, 38: 499.

ST. JOHN, B.E., 1970. Ultra-trace element analysis of carbonate rocks by APDC–MIBK extraction and atomic absorption spectrophotometry. *J. Sedimet. Petrol.*, 40: 537–541.

SCARBOROUGH, J.M., BINGHAM, C.D., and DE VRIES, P.F., 1967. Determination of trace metallic impurities in high purity sodium using atomic absorption spectrometry. *Anal. Chem.*, 39 (12): 1394–1397.

SLAVIN, S. and SATTUR, T.W., 1968. Spectral interference of lead on antimony. *At. Absorpt. Newsl., Perkin–Elmer Corp.*, 7 (5): 99.

SPENCER, B.W. and BREWER, T.G., 1969. The distribution of copper, zinc, and nickel in sea water of the Gulf of Maine and the Sargasso Sea. *Geochim. Cosmochim. Acta*, 33: 325.

SUGAWARA, V. and YAMAZAKI, V., 1970. The determination of heavy metals and dust fall by atomic absorption spectrophotometry. *Taike Osen Kenkyu.*, 4 (2): 182–187.

SWINDER, R.T., 1968. Atomic absorption determination of platinum in geochemical and mining samples. *At. Absorpt. Newsl., Perkin–Elmer Corp.*, 7: 111–112.

THILLIEZ, G., 1969. Quantitative analysis of metals by atomic absorption in industrial medicine, 1. Application to quantitative analysis of organic lead in the air of workshop environments. *Arch. Mal., Prof. Med. Trav. Secur. Soc.*, 31 (3): 133–140.

THOMAS, P.E. and CHUMNONG, H., 1969. The atomic absorption determination of beryllium in beryl. *Resonance Lines*, 1 (5): 5–6 (Publication of Varian Techtron Inc.).

THOMAS, P.E., SANDERS, J.B. and CHUMNONG, H., 1969. The determination of tungsten in wolframite by atomic absorption spectrophotometry. *Resonance Lines,* 1(3): 5–7 (Publication of Varian Techtron Inc.).

THOMPSON, C.E., NAKAGAWA, H.M. and VAN SICKLE, G.H., 1968. Rapid analysis for gold in geologic materials. *U.S. Geol. Surv. Prof. Pap.*, 600-B: 130–132.

VAN LOON, J.C., 1969. Atomic absorption determination of iridium in precious metal-bearing concentrate. *At. Absorpt. Newsl., Perkin–Elmer Corp.*, 8: 6–7.

VASAK, V., 1968. Atomic absorption spectrophotometry: its use in industrial toxicology. *Czech. Hyg.*, 13 (2): 105–110.

WARD, F.N. and NAKAGAWA, H.M., 1967. Atomic absorption determination of bismuth in altered rocks. *U.S. Geol. Surv., Prof. Pap.*, 575-D: 239–241.

WEST, F.K., WEST, P.W., and RAMAKRISHNA, T.V., 1967. Stabilization and determination of traces of silver in waters. *Environ. Sci. Tech.*, 1 (9): 717–724.

WINEFORDNER, J.D., 1969. New atomic spectroscopic methods for trace analysis. *Proc. Off. Aerosp. Res.*, 1: D 1 – D 19 (OAR 69-0011).

ZWEIBAUM, F. and MOORHEAD, J., 1967. A multi element atomic absorption analyzer. *At. Absorpt. Newsl. Perkin–Elmer Corp.*, 6 (6): 134.

Index